G000071515

PECKHAM CRY

PECKHAM CRY

Janice S Cooke

Pharaoh Press

Peckham Cry
ISBN 1 901442 05 5

First published in 1998 by Pharoah Press

Copyright © Janice S. Cooke

Condition of Sale
This book is sold subject to the condition that it shall not,
by way of trade or otherwise, be lent, re-sold, hired out
or otherwise circulated without the publisher's prior
consent in any form of binding or cover other than that in
which it is published and without a similar condition
including this condition being imposed on the
subsequent purchaser.

Printed in Great Britain by Short Run Press Ltd, Exeter, Devon.

Chapter One

Sylvia walked slowly home from school that cold December afternoon in 1951, wondering why it was that some of the other children should be so mean to her. It wasn't as if she had done anything wrong . . . well leastways, not at school. As she walked, she made sure that her feet only touched the paving slabs and not the lines between them. She thought about her home. Things were not quite right there, but if you'd asked her what the problem was, she would have found it hard to explain. She also wondered whether her father would come home from work again with that funny smell on his breath. He always tried to kiss her and put his tongue in her mouth. She found it all rather bewildering, but she liked it when he used to give her a threepenny piece to bribe her not to tell anyone about their little 'tickles.' It had been going on for as long as she cared to remember, and she was now just turned seven.

As she came around the corner from Maxted Road into Nutbrook Street, her heart gave a lurch when she spotted some of the bigger girls and boys from her primary school leaning against the pillar box laughing together. She lowered her head and tried to quicken her pace.

"Goofy teeth! Goofy teeth! Cat got your tongue?" they taunted, linking arms in front of her so as to bar her way.

"Please let me go! My mother will wonder where I am."

"Oh, she will, will she?" said Carol Baker, who seemed to be the ringleader. "I shouldn't think she even cares about you. Look at the state of you! You look like a ragamuffin! Your hair is horrible, you're skinny and you have a great big tidemark round the back of your neck. Pooh, you stink! Sylvia wets the bed!"

At this all the other children joined in, chanting: "Sylvia wets the bed! Sylvia wets the bed!"

"I don't!" cried Sylvia, raising a grubby hand to brush the tears from her eyes.

"Come on, let's leave her alone."

This last speaker was a ginger-haired boy whom Sylvia thought was called Eric Sweeney. He used to smile at her when she was in school and she was fascinated by his freckles and his blue eyes which were fringed with pale blond lashes. She wondered why his eyelashes weren't ginger as well.

"No fear! We want to see her cry and run home and tell her Mummy – her dear Mummy, who couldn't care less!"

They all began to punch her, and Sylvia, to her embarrassment, felt a warm trickle run down her legs.

"Look! Cry Baby's wet herself!" shrieked her tormentors. "Now she really will smell awful. We'd better go before we cop it."

With a final punch, then a kick for good measure, they all ran off leaving Sylvia trembling and feeling very uncomfortable with her wet knickers slapping against her legs. Her main worry now was how to get indoors without being seen by her mother. She was frightened of her mother, who would beat her for the slightest thing, and she knew she would be annoyed with her for wetting her knickers.

"Are you all right?"

Sylvia looked up. She was being addressed by a girl she knew as Veronica. They were in the same class at school, but Sylvia didn't really mix with the other children as she was a bit of a 'loner'. She was also tremendously shy and felt unable to make friends. Veronica, like her, had been bullied in the past and just because she wore National Health glasses. Unfortunately, they gave her an owl – like appearance which wasn't helped by the way she twisted her head to one side whenever she spoke to anyone. The glasses were ugly things with round metal frames and, to make matters worse, she also had to wear a pink patch over one of her eyes to correct a rather pronounced squint. However, she had stood up to the bullying and now they left her alone.

"Thank you for asking," said Sylvia. "I'm just frightened that I'll get told off for – well, you know . . ."

Veronica was very understanding.

"Look," she said, "why don't you come home with me and we'll get you tidied up first? Then your mother won't have any cause to be angry with you. I only live just over there." She pointed as she spoke to a pre-fab which stood on a small allotment with about six others.

Sylvia looked at her gratefully; shyly, she took the proffered hand in her own rather grubby one and they made their way to Veronica's house.

"Mum, it's me!" Veronica called. "I'm home."

Her mother came hurrying out of the kitchen, hair pinned neatly with Kirby Grips against the side of her head.

"I'm very pleased to meet you, whispered Sylvia, holding her hands behind her back so that Mrs. Coles wouldn't see the damp patch at the back of her frock.

"Would you like to stay and have a bite of tea with us?" the lady enquired. "I've made loads of fish paste sandwiches and a chocolate sponge cake, even if it is made with dried eggs. Veronica, and Eddie, that's her brother, have simply the most enormous appetites, only you wouldn't think so, would you?" She laughed and looked at her daughter, who was as slim as she had

4

once been. "Veronica takes after her dad, you know," she continued. "Why, he eats like a horse and never puts on an ounce of fat, unlike me!"

Sylvia thought she was lovely, anyway, and would have given her right arm to have a mother like Veronica had.

"I'm sorry, I can't stay to tea today," she replied. "My mother will be wondering where I am as it is, but perhaps you will ask me another time."

"Come and look at my bedroom," Veronica put in, diplomatically. "Then I'll walk you to the top of the road."

Veronica's bedroom was at the end of the small hallway. It was very small, but neat and tidy. Veronica went over to a chest of drawers which stood underneath the window and, bending down, opened a drawer and took out a pair of navy blue knickers.

"I think these'll fit you," she announced. "If you take off your wet ones, I'll put them in with my washing so no one will ever know."

"You are kind. I don't know what I would have done if you hadn't come along," said Sylvia gratefully, hastily doing as she was told. "What shall I do with these?" she asked. She stood there, sheepishly, holding the wet knickers away from her with the tips of the fingers.

"Just pop them in here," Veronica said, holding out a paper bag. "I'll see that they get washed without your being found out. It wasn't your fault. I'd have done the same if it had been me they picked on."

Presently Sylvia said goodbye to Mrs. Coles, and

the two girls walked arm in arm to the corner of Adys Road, which led into Keston Road where Sylvia lived.

"Are you sure you'll be all right now?" Veronica asked solicitously.

"Yes, thank you. Oh, and by the way, did you mean what you said about me being your bestest friend?"

"Of course I did, silly! If you like, I'll come and call for you in the morning and we can walk to school together."

Sylvia thought for a moment about what her mother would say. She knew she didn't approve of people who lived in prefabricated houses; she always said they were little more than gypsies.

"No, you'd better not," she replied hurriedly, "but I tell you what. I'll meet you on the corner by the post box at half past eight, if that's all right with you."

Veronica looked puzzled by this, but her face soon cleared.

"Yes, all right then," she said. "See you tomorrow." With a cheery wave she turned and ran back the way she had come.

Sylvia started to run towards her house; this was only one of a terrace, but it was quite large because it was the end one in the road. It had two storeys in the front, and three at the back. She stopped suddenly when she saw her mother standing on the doorstep with her arms folded menacingly across her chest; then she went on more slowly, dreading the telling-off that was sure to follow.

"And just where have you been until this time?"

Mrs. Short demanded.

"I – I just . . . just . . . " stammered Sylvia; then she started again. "Miss Wilson kept me behind to do some reading for the school play."

"Oh yes, a likely story! If you've been playing with the other children, I'll let your father deal with you when he comes home."

Poor Sylvia! For the life of her, she couldn't understand why she was never allowed to play with other children, bring them home for tea and let them stay overnight with her. The girls at school were always talking about parties, but she had never been to one in her life.

"Get in and changed before tea. I wasn't going to give you any, considering how late you are. I thought if you're this late, then you couldn't be very hungry."

Sylvia glanced at her mother, noticing how tired she looked. Why couldn't she smile once in a while, or better than that, say something nice? She must have been an attractive woman once upon a time. Now her hair was turning grey, her brown eyes never sparkled, and she had tiny lines running down the sides of her mouth. It all added up to the appearance of someone who was discontented with life in general.

Indeed, Sylvia could remember a time when her mother had been happy. It was all a bit vague, but it had something to do with a baby called Richard, who she thought was her brother. He was with them for quite some time, until one day when she woke up he wasn't there any more. She had asked where he was but all she could remember was her mother crying. It was all so long ago now. Maybe if she tried really hard, she would remember it one day.

She ran quickly inside, remembering to dodge the cuff that would be aimed at her, but she wasn't quick enough and her mother's hand caught her on the side of her cheek and brought tears to her eyes.

Rushing up the stairs, she almost knocked over her brother John in her haste. John was eighteen months older than her and could be a bit of a bully. She knew her parents liked him better than her, so she tried really hard to do well at school and make them proud of her. She already belonged to the library at Grove Vale; she had been with them since she was just turned four. She had been able to read before she started school and nobody had taught her. She just seemed to pick it up naturally. As you couldn't join the library until you were five, her headmistress had made special arrangements for her and now she could take two books home each week. She was allowed to go all by herself on the tram and paid one penny for the privilege. Once in the library, she would browse around taking in the smell of fresh polish and musty old books. She was so happy that she could have spent all day in there. Oh, how she loved reading, especially Enid Blyton books! In her bedroom she had a small rug on the floor beside the bed: she would sit on that and wish it would go to magical faraway places. Of course, the rug never flew, but she would pretend that it did, and they went on some fantastic adventures together in her dreams.

Sylvia's bedroom was a small but cosy room at the top of the house, next to the bathroom. She had a bed with springs, on which was placed a horsehair mattress. This could be uncomfortable, as sometimes the hairs from the mattress would poke through the sheets and dig into her whilst she slept. What her mother didn't know was that Sylvia rarely slept in her bed, preferring to lie on her magic rug and leave the bed free for all her soft toys which she felt sorry for, especially in the winter. So she would take them and tuck them up in her bed, placing them in rows together according to size and friendship, because they each had their own special friend. Then she would kiss them goodnight three times before pulling off the candlewick bed-spread and covering herself with it on the rug on the floor. She always made sure that her parents were in bed when this happened and she would be up early in the morning to creep back into bed between the toys. There wasn't enough room for all of them, but Sylvia didn't mind sleeping on the floor as long as her toys were nice and warm . . .

She changed quickly and hurried downstairs, hoping her mother would keep her tea for her. It wouldn't be the first time that she had been forced to go without, but today she really did feel hungry. She couldn't help thinking about Veronica and those fish paste sand-wiches and that chocolate cake. There was nothing like that for her at home, but she did have sandwiches made with spam and some lemon curd tarts. She had a glass of water to drink as she did with all meals now, since the taste of tea made her retch. It was unfortunate, because she used to like tea until the day when she didn't feel very well. Her mother said there was nothing wrong with her and she could jolly well sit there and finish her breakfast, which was kippers and a cup of tea. She knew it was useless to argue, so wearily she had picked at the food and placed small pieces in her mouth. The kippers and tea were quite cold and she gagged with each mouthful. She managed to finish it before rushing to the outside lavvy to be violently sick. From that day on, she had not touched a kipper or a cup of tea.

'Food fads', Mrs. Short had called it: she said she was lucky to be having a cup of tea what with war rationing still being on. Sylvia, however, was quite content to drink water; she could occasionally sneak some fruit juice into it.

She was helping herself to a second sandwich when she suddenly found the temerity to ask: "What's a baa-stard? Only somebody at school said that I . . ." Her voice faded away as she saw the look on her mother's face.

There was a stony silence. You could have cut the atmosphere with a knife.

"Bed! Get up those stairs to bed, right now!" Mrs. Short's face was livid as she spat the words between clenched teeth.

Sylvia, too frightened to repeat the question, ran from the room, bewildered by the fuss. She didn't realise that it was a naughty word, a forbidden word. It was just that somebody had called her that at school today and wanted to know what it meant. In her fright she pulled her clothes off and got quickly into bed, forgetting all about the toys and even her cold water wash tonight. She drew the bedcovers up over her head and, shutting her eyes tight, willed sleep to come.

She must have nodded off, for the next thing she heard was her name being called gently. She opened her eyes and looked straight up into her father's face. He smiled down at her.

"Your mother says that you said a naughty word today, and that I should punish you, but I don't want to because you're my very own special little girl and I love you. Will you tell me that you love me, too?" With that he went over to her bedroom door and shouted down: "Won't be long, love! I'll have a quick shave while I'm up here." He listened until he heard her muffled answer and then shut the door stealthily. "Now then, you're going to have to pretend that I have hit you and you start crying. All right?"

Sylvia nodded, only too happy to comply with her father's wishes. He smacked the pillow and she let out a yell. This happened four times in all and it must have sounded quite convincing to the ears listening downstairs.

Satisfied that she had been duly 'punished', her father made Sylvia stand up in bed and put her arms around his neck and tell him that she loved him.

"I do love you, Daddy, you know that."

"Say it again," he said, his breath now coming in short gasps as he fondled himself while darting his tongue in and out of his daughter's mouth. He lowered his head to her tiny breasts, which hadn't even started to form yet, and began to lick the little pimples. Then he went lower still and started to kiss her 'muff', as he called it. Sylvia felt no sensation whatsoever; if she shuddered, it was because of the coldness of the room. But her father shuddered, too, and looking down, she saw that his hand was wet, with something white and sticky on it.

"I get that way because I love you," he said, by way of explanation.

Sylvia thought it was a funny thing to get because you loved someone. She didn't say anything, but just lay back in bed and let him tuck her up. She didn't really like him 'doing things' to her, but she felt unable to stop him. He was also kinder to her than her mother and she did truly love him. She drifted off into a troubled sleep and the last thing she heard was the two of them laughing together downstairs. She thought that was nice because there wasn't much laughter in that house. Perhaps things might get better if she showed her father that she loved him. Normally after such an incident, the atmosphere at home started to improve.

Chapter Two

Next morning, Sylvia was up early and she raced to the bathroom to have her wash, paying particular attention to behind her ears and round the back of her neck. The water was icy cold, so she quickly got dressed and went downstairs for breakfast. The living room was chilly, because the fire in the boiler had gone out overnight. Her mother was in the scullery – and, what a surprise! She actually looked happy today! She even had a smile for Sylvia.

"Have some nice hot porridge inside you," she said. "It's very cold outside today. There was a heavy frost last night. If you look carefully on the window, you will see the mark of Jack Frost."

Sylvia felt warmed by this consideration. She was

also happy because in less than an hour she would be meeting her friend.

"There's a good girl. You've eaten it all up. Now, don't forget to put your hat and scarf on. Oh! And have you remembered to put your liberty bodice on?"

"Yes, Mum, I have."

Sylvia secretly wished her mother didn't fuss so, because although she had her faults, she still managed to keep them warm and fed. She was an expert seamstress and most of Sylvia's clothes were hand-me-downs adapted for her use. Unfortunately, Mrs. Short used to make them a little on the long side, which of course didn't help matters at school when the other children used to poke fun at her.

"I wish you wouldn't call me 'Mum'," said her mother. I think it sounds so common. Don't forget to go to the toilet before you go to school."

Sylvia trudged outside to the lavvy. She hated it. It was so cold out there and full of spiders. She had to stay out there a fair while, otherwise her mother would say that she couldn't possibly have done a 'number two' in so short a space of time and promptly dispatch her outside again. Of course she couldn't go, but she pretended that she had, and wiping her bottom on a sheet of newspaper that was hanging along with several others on a piece of string. Sometimes out of boredom, she would read the newsprint, but today was too cold; and anyway, she had her bestest friend to meet.

She could see Veronica waiting by the post box as she

rounded the corner. She sped to meet her and tucking her arm through her friend's, they were laughing and chattering at once.

"Come to the shop with me," said Sylvia. "I've got a threepenny bit. You can help me to spend it."

The shop was opposite the school, and was run by an elderly woman with snowy white hair. The children used to call her Florrie, but nobody was sure whether that was her real name. It was a tiny shop, but immediately you went inside, you were overwhelmed by the smell and array of sweets. Sylvia liked the big glass bottles that were displayed on a high shelf just inside the door. They were filled with coloured water, one red, one blue and one green. Once she had asked Florrie if she could buy a penny drink of the red one and Florrie had said:

"Bless you, child, they are for display purposes only."

Sylvia didn't know what this meant, but she gathered that they were not for drinking and settled for a Tizer instead.

"Good morning, girls. What can I get you today?"

Sylvia thought long and hard, before deciding that she would like a penn'orth of sherbet. Veronica was of the same mind for herself, so that left one penny, which they decided to spend on two fruit salads and two black jacks. Florrie weighed out some lemon sherbet crystals into silver scales. Then, picking up a sheet of newspaper, she twisted it into a cone shape, making sure that the bottom was folded over before

15

pouring the sherbet into it. She made another one and in each case added a little extra sherbet for good measure.

The friends were delighted with the transaction and went outside to share the other sweets, hoping they had time to eat them before the school bell went.

The sherbet left a stain on their fingers, so they pretended it was caused by nicotine. They had got this idea from seeing their fathers' fingers; and smoking seemed a pretty grown up thing to do. They went into the school playground and told everybody that they had been smoking. Some of the children were wide-eyed with admiration, but the older ones knew it was sherbet and told them so. All in all the day passed well; and although Sylvia saw the children who had bullied her the day before, they seemed not to want to bother today, apart from the odd poking out of a tongue.

That evening, as they parted on the usual corner, the two girls felt sad. Another weekend was coming up and they would miss each other. It would have been nice for Sylvia if her mother had allowed her to go to a friend's house, or have friends to visit her; but there was no chance of that. Veronica was aware of the ban and, not wanting to spoil their friendship, she decided not to mention it; but sooner or later she would have to. After all, there was no point in having a best friend if you could only see her at school.

Sylvia hated the weekends. It was always the same thing; pictures at the Odeon on Saturday afternoon and a trip to Oxford Street on Sunday to window shop. She hated the walk down Ondine Road which led to the Odeon Cinema. It seemed to go on forever, and just lately something else had begun to happen which invariably caused friction. They would leave the cinema at around five o'clock to begin the return journey, and the minute they got to the junction of Ondine Road and Adys Road, Sylvia would wet her knickers. She had tried holding herself through her coat, but it hadn't worked. Four times in succession this had happened; and it happened again today. Mrs. Short began to rant and rave at her, right there in the street, as soon as she found out, and Sylvia cried and felt so ashamed, but she couldn't help it. She didn't do it deliberately, but her mother did not understand. Once they reached home, she would run upstairs in disgrace without any tea.

Now Mrs. Short had stumbled on a new trick, which was to make Sylvia go to bed with her wet knickers on her head. The logic behind this was to make the knickers dry enough to wear the next day. But it was humiliating for the child, for not only did it make her hair smell, it caused the children at school to hold their noses in disgust whenever she walked by.

On this occasion it wasn't her father who crept into her room, it was her brother John, who pinched and pulled her hair, and called her a 'dirty little guttersnipe'. Sometimes she felt as if she hated him because he was stronger than her and she couldn't fight him back. He would pick on her when they were left in the care of their grandmother while their parents went to the local pub, the 'Gowlett Arms'. When the grandmother wasn't looking, John would punch her on the arm, and she had the bruises to show for it.

She was hoping it would rain the next day, for if it did there would be no window shopping in Oxford Street and she could avoid disgracing herself further. Although it was only a sixpenny ride away on a number 12 bus, she always got sick. She would try to hold it in until they got off the bus, but she succeeded only in throwing up over the floor of the bus. She knew it embarrassed her family, but it was even worse for her. She thought she must be jinxed, for she didn't understand why she did it. The only escape was if she did not got to the cinema or on the bus. So she prayed and, and as luck would have it, her prayers were granted, for when she woke it was teeming down with rain. She said a silent thank you to the unseen person in the sky, and spent a quiet day in the end playing with a jigsaw puzzle.

The next morning Veronica wanted to know what she had done at the weekend.

"I had a lovely time," Sylvia lied. She didn't dare say what had really happened, for fear that if she did, Veronica wouldn't want to be friends with her any more.

* * *

It was nearly Christmas and the school was busy making preparations for the Nativity Play. Both Sylvia and Veronica were in it and the parents were all invited. Veronica's mother planned to be there, and she was looking forward to meeting Mrs. Short with a view to asking her to come to the little party she was holding for her children; but in the event, Sylvia's mother didn't come.

Christmas day dawned and Sylvia went down with chicken pox. Not a Christmas went by without her having some illness or another. Her mother thought that it was too much excitement which caused it, and became quite sympathetic towards her daughter. Opening her presents, Sylvia was delighted with the teddy bear that her parents had bought for her. There was also a jigsaw puzzle, crayons and colouring book, chocolate, and orange and some nuts, along with some sensible things like a new scarf, gloves and socks which came from her Auntie Eva who lived in Ivydale Road.

Sylvia watched anxiously while her parents opened their presents from her. For her mother, there was a golliwog made out of pipe cleaners and wool. She hadn't exactly made it herself. She had found it lying around at school and thought nobody would miss it. For her father, she had made a lot of 'spills' out of paper which he could put in the fire to lit his pipe with, thus saving having to buy matches. She had also covered a jam jar with coloured paper, which made a handy container to put his 'spills' in.

"Thank you, my little girl!" Mr. Short appeared to be highly delighted with his present.

Her mother had a different reaction. "Are you telling me you made this at school?"

"N-n-not exactly . . ." stammered Sylvia. "I found it lying on the floor and I thought you would like it."

"That is called stealing, my girl. Do you hear me? Stealing!" She shook her so hard that Sylvia's teeth started to rattle.

"Don't do that, pet," said Mr. Short. "You know she's not very well."

Her mother, not to be placated, was unwilling to drop the subject. "I shall sort this one out when that child goes back to school," she threatened. "I'll have a word with her teacher. This sort of thing has to be nipped in the bud before it gets out of hand. We don't want a thief in the family. Oh, the shame she brings on us! If it's not one thing it's another. I am at my wits end with her."

"Sshh, pet! Don't upset yourself. I'm sure Sylvia didn't mean any harm by it."

True to her word, when school resumed in January, Mrs. Short marched off to see the headmistress and gave the golliwog back. Apparently one of the other children had made it for her mother, but when she had come to take it home and wrap it up for Christmas, she could not find it. The headmistress was very strict about things like stealing and took notice of what Sylvia's mother said. By way of punishment, Sylvia was sent to Miss Clark's classroom where all the naughty children were sent.

Everyone was frightened of Miss Clark, who looked so old to all the pupils. She was in fact, only in her forties but she wore drab grey frocks, clasped in the middle by a metal belt, and her face was stern. When she was angry, a little tic would start at the corners of her mouth, which gave her an even grimmer expression.

"Sit over in the corner and memorise 'Praise my soul the King of Heaven'," she told Sylvia. "You will find it on page 92."

Sylvia dutifully obeyed, but this was an easy task for her. She loved hymns and knew practically every one by heart. Soon she was raising her hand.

"Please, Miss, I can recite it for you now."

Miss Clark looked at her in surprise and disbelief. "Very well," she said finally, hoping to catch her out.

But Sylvia was indeed word-perfect and poor Miss Clark had no option but to send her back to her own classroom.

This feat was of a piece with Sylvia's other accomplishment. She was easily the brightest child in the school, which was surprising considering the traumatic life she led at home. She won prize after prize for essays and her reading was superb. She was beginning to enjoy school now that she had a friend and the bullying had almost stopped. She was made milk monitor and because of that she had first refusal if there was any milk left over. She was always first in the queue for her Cod Liver Oil and Malt in the morning and licked the spoon with relish. The only cloud over her days was when she had to go home. Holidays were a severe trial. The days dragged and she could hardly wait for the school term to begin again.

One day Veronica told her she had something to show her. After school they went back to her house and from the top of the wardrobe in her bedroom, Veronica took down a cage. Sylvia gasped in surprise, for in the cage was a tiny, perfect, white mouse, pink-nosed with whiskers twitching.

"It's lovely!" she finally blurted out, filled with envy.

At home, she tentatively asked her mother if she could have one too. Much to her surprise, Mrs. Short agreed and the next Saturday found Sylvia clutching a sixpence and setting off to the pet shop which was in the arcade in Rye Lane. She chose one just like her friend's and promptly called him Mickey. Her father made her a cage out of wood and Mickey was placed in it, in the garden shed. Every day she would peek at him before going to school and the regular task of cleaning out the cage was left to her. Once, however, she noticed that there were tiny, pink, hairless scraps in the cage, six in all. Her brother came to look and began to poke them about. He didn't know what they were, so he ran to fetch their mother, who announced that 'Mickey' had had babies. Sadly, because the mouse had been disturbed, the babies disappeared. The children weren't to know that the mother had eaten most of them and tossed the others out of the nest.

One day, Sylvia had run out of the food she used to buy for her pet, so she went to the larder to get some cornflakes, which the mouse seemed to enjoy. She didn't realise that her mother was watching her, but on her return from school she had to pay a visit to the lavvy and there, to her horror, she found the mouse lying dead on top of the water. Bursting into floods of tears, she ran indoors.

"I don't want you stealing food from me to feed your pet," her mother told her coldly. "If you must have food, then ask in the proper manner."

Sylvia thought it was horrid of her to do such a thing; she also knew that she would never be given another mouse as a pet. She had loved that mouse, told it all her secrets and also on a few occasions, had taken it to school with her without Mrs. Short finding out. Or maybe she had found out? She always seemed to know everything; but in this case Sylvia could not be sure. She always got the blame when things went missing from home. One time it was money and another time some fruit. Sylvia had a sneaking suspicion that her grandmother was doing it, but this was hard to believe. Her grandmother was very old and not in the best of health. When Mr. Short began to decorate Sylvia's bedroom, Sylvia was put in with her. She liked her granny's room as there was a big pendulum clock in there which used to make a comforting tick-tock and lull her off to sleep.

It could not be denied that her granny did do funny things. They used to attend the Amott Road Baptist Church every Sunday morning, and when the collection plate came round she would always drop a sixpence in and take five pence back. Sylvia wanted to join the Girl's Brigade, but Mrs. Short objected on the grounds that it was common to parade around the streets carrying a banner . . . .

Sylvia awoke to a commotion in the bedroom and saw the family doctor bending over her granny and shaking his head sadly. Her father picked her up and moved her into her brother's bedroom, where she promptly fell back to sleep. The next morning she was told that her granny had died and gone to heaven. This saddened her, as she had been fond of the old lady. They used to have fun singing together. One song in particular was called 'Just a Song at Twilight'; Sylvia found this very moving. Her granny would tell her tales about the 'old days' and the child would listen spellbound to some of the antics they had got up to. Yes, she would definitely miss her granny!

Chapter Three

It was the first of June, 1953, and the day before the Coronation. Princess Elizabeth was to be crowned Queen in Westminster Abbey. The children were to be given the day off school to celebrate and all over Britain street parties were being organised. John and Sylvia had each been given a commemorative mug costing one and sixpence, and they were both excited about the party that was to be held in their street.

"Pop round to Maisie and get some horseradish sauce," her mother told Sylvia. "And while you're there, take the vinegar bottle and let her fill it up with some of the malt stuff she has in the barrel."

Clutching the money her mother had given her, Sylvia raced round to the little shop in Amott Road.

As she did so, she could see the long trestle tables being set up and the red, white and blue flags proudly flying between the groups of houses. Such excitement! She ran into the shop almost dazzled by it all.

Maisie, a very large plump woman, with a mass of curly hair which always seemed to stick up from her head, laughed when she saw the child's eager look. Everyone was feeling the same that day. She herself had just taken delivery of a television set. It was a G.E.C. one and had cost sixty-four pounds, six shillings and twopence. It was advertised as a 'New Big Screen'; it was in fact a twelve inch screen built into a walnut cabinet. Not many people had television sets, so Maisie was proud of her new possession. Her family, who were grown up and scattered over various parts of the country, would be coming to visit tomorrow to watch the Coronation which was being broadcast live.

"Mother says will you fill this up with vinegar? And also, can I have some . . . er . . ." Sylvia racked her brains as she tried to think what it was that her mother had asked her to get. She couldn't for the life of her remember whether it was horseradish sauce or mint sauce. In the end she plumped for mint sauce and, clutching the vinegar bottle in one hand and the mint sauce in the other, set off back to home.

Of course, an unholy row broke out. Anyone would have thought that Sylvia had committed the crime of the century. The upshot of it was that her mug was taken away; she was also told that she could not go to the street party, but would be sent to bed instead.

That night her father arrived to 'punish' her again and this time she did get beaten with the long thin cane that was kept inside the wardrobe in her parents' bedroom. She lay there, quietly sobbing to herself; she could feel the angry red weals it had raised. She could hardly sleep on her back because of them. She was not resentful. She thought she was a naughty child and this was what she deserved. After her father had punished her, he kissed her and told her to stand up, which she did. This time he undid the front of his trousers and made her take hold of a long soft pink thing. He told her to rub it gently, then kiss it. As she did, it began to grow bigger and her father moaned. He told her to rub it harder and what a pretty girl she was. Sylvia obeyed him, and rubbed so hard that her hand started to ache. Suddenly she felt a sticky wetness and, looking down, saw the white stuff again. She gazed at her father trustingly; now she knew he loved her because he had said so before when he too had that white sticky stuff on his hand. He told her what a good girl she was before taking out his hanky to wipe her hand. She settled down for sleep still smarting from the caning, but content in the knowledge that he would love her forever.

The next day when she awoke she noted to her satisfaction that it was overcast and raining. Then she admonished herself for her wicked thoughts. She knew that it would spoil all the preparations for the street party that people had worked so hard for, weeks beforehand. She was allowed up for breakfast; then she had to go back to bed. she could hear the music in the street below and pushed her fingers really tightly into her ears to block out the noise. Her parents and her brother went out; when she was satisfied that the street door had closed, she crept from the bedroom and along the corridor to sit on the stairs and look out of the upstairs landing window. She couldn't see much as the window overlooked the bombed site that was on the corner of Amott Road. On the rare occasions when she was allowed out, that was where she and her brother would play, amongst all the rubble, risking the chance of getting dirty and being told off yet again. It was always her that got all the blame, never her brother; but really he was just as naughty as she was. Maybe if she had been a boy, she thought, she would not be punished as much as she was.

To her astonishment she noticed that a man was working on the bomb site. She had overheard her parents talking about two houses which were to be built there, but up till now she had paid no real attention to the matter. Further on down the street, people were laughing and cheering despite the rain. A mass of umbrellas were waving gaily. Her family were nowhere to be seen and she guessed that they were further up the street. How long she sat there for, she had no idea, but gradually she became aware that she was cold and her back was aching. She went back to bed and lay still for some time before taking a book from the cupboard to read. It was all about a magical 'Faraway Tree', which you could climb and find yourself in another land full of surprises. Oh, how she wished she had a tree like that in her garden! Any time she had problems, she could climb the tree and disappear. Perhaps then they would worry about her, and be sorry that she had gone away.

Some time later she heard a noise downstairs and realised that the party must have finished. Her bedroom door opened slowly and John came in clutching bars of chocolates and a bright red balloon. Uncharacteristically, he gave her one of the chocolate bars, saying: "Don't tell Mum! She'll kill me if she finds out." He then spent the next few minutes telling her about how super it had all been and what she had missed, until Sylvia became quite miserable.

Mrs. Short suddenly appeared and told John to go down for his tea. He protested that he wasn't hungry after eating sandwiches, cake, ice cream and jelly. Sylvia was thankful that she had the presence of mind hide the chocolate under pillow so that she could eat it later. Her mother said she could get dressed and go down for a bite of tea as well. Sylvia thought she would never forget the coronation, and she never did.

★   ★   ★

By the summer of 1954, there were two new houses standing on the old bomb site. One day when Sylvia was sitting on the landing, she noticed that people were moving in. It looked as if both families had children, and she was very interested to see that the house nearer to the corner had a little girl of about her own age. The girl was dressed rather prettily; she had short blonde curly hair and was very slim, almost fragile. She spotted Sylvia at the window looking down and waved to her. Sylvia waved back delightedly, before rushing into her bedroom to find something to give to her in the hope of sealing their friendship. All she could lay her hands on was a comic entitled 'School Friend'. Hastily she wrote a note: "Dear little girl next door, my name is Sylvia and I am nearly ten. Do you want to be my friend?" Then, slipping downstairs, while her mother was busy in the scullery, she let herself out of the house and popped the comic and the note through next door's letter box.

She had a reply the next day which simply stated that Yes, June would like to be her friend. Sylvia was over the moon and gave Veronica the good news. Veronica was none too happy about this as Sylvia had been her best friend for three years, and she didn't want to lose her.

Alas, things were changing in their lives. Veronica wasn't as clever as Sylvia and it looked as if they would be going their separate ways when they left junior school. Veronica would be going to Peckham Girls' School at the bottom of Rye Lane; but Sylvia had her heart set on going to a grammar school. Various ones had mentioned, including Mary Datchelor at Camberwell, James Alleyn's at Dulwich and Honor Oak near Peckham Rye Park.

June, meanwhile, attended a special school for delicate girls as she had had tuberculosis and was still very frail. Her mother had said that she would be attending a normal secondary school when 1955 came. Luckily for Sylvia, June's mother and Mrs. Short had become quite friendly, which meant that the girls could play together, and even visit each other's houses for tea. Soon they became firm friends and shared all sorts of secrets. Only one thing was never mentioned: the relationship between Sylvia and her father was a dreadful secret never to be told to anyone.

Poor Veronica was really left out of it now. All along, it had just been stupid snobbery that prevented their relationship from blossoming. Mrs. Short didn't approve of pre-fabricated houses; she didn't mind being seen in a house that was newly built. June's father was a builder; he had not only built their house and one for his sister, but he had contracts for others on old bombed sites all over London. They were quite rich by the day's standards, but June was totally unspoilt by it all. She was their only daughter and they lavished love and attention on her.

What was really nice was the fact that they also gave a lot of time and care to Sylvia. They would take the girls out to Southend-on-Sea, where they all had a jolly time. At night the trees were covered with fairy lights and they would walk along to 'Peter Pan's Playground'. Sylvia would return home from these trips with her fair complexion burnt red from the sun and her mother would tut over her and smother her in calamine lotion.

Soon it was time to take the eleven plus exam which would decide which school Sylvia would go to.

As the pupils filed into the hall where they would sit the exam, school pens, rulers and pencil cases were taken away and each child was issued with a number. Sylvia was given two pencils which she found very degrading as she hadn't written in pencil for years. No-one smiled. The headmistress came in with a large brown envelope. She told everyone that this was the most important day of their lives and that they were to 'DO THEIR BEST'. Sylvia thought she would die. She was so nervous she could hardly hold the pencils, but she was determined to do her best . . . and she did.

When the results came through, she found she had won a 'Governors Place', which meant that she could go to any of the top grammar schools. John had already been placed at Adys Road Boys, having failed his eleven plus, the previous year. It wasn't as if he were stupid, he was a whiz kid at anything electronic. He had just finished making a 'crystal set', and they used to listen to 'Journey into Space' on it; but he was useless at school work.

Mrs. Short decided, when she saw the results, that what was good enough for John was good enough for Sylvia, too. There were numerous arguments about it, mainly revolving around things like school uniform and sports equipment, such as hockey sticks. Mrs. Short didn't want all the extra expense. So instead of going to her beloved Honor Oak, which she had set her heart on, Sylvia found that she would be attending Friern Road Secondary Modern, which was an all-girls' school. She was so disappointed that she went to bed and sobbed her heart out.

"Never mind," June consoled her the next day.

"That's the school I think Mum and Dad are sending me to. At least we shall be together."

★　★　★

It was a sad day for Sylvia when the term ended and she had to say goodbye to her friends. She knew that wouldn't be seeing much of Veronica as their schools were miles apart. Some of the other girls were going to Friern – among them Carol Baker, who had used to pick on her all those years ago, but was now a friend – so at least there would be people there that she knew. Just the prospect of the long summer holiday was bleak and she couldn't wait to start her new school in September.

Veronica walked home with her as always, but today they were both quiet. Sylvia had more freedom now that she was getting older, but the ban on visiting 'pre-fabricated houses' still remained, and she had more sense than to disobey her mother. She was allowed to play at the swing park at Goose Green, and told Veronica as much.

"All right," said Veronica , head bowed slightly to one side. "I shall make sure that I come up there most days, just in case you are there."

She had never broached the subject of why she was not allowed to go to Sylvia's house or vice versa, but it hadn't stopped them being friends for nearly four years. They had shared lots of secrets, had loads of fun, and when one of them had a piece of bubblegum, she even used to take a piece out of her mouth and offer it to the other. It didn't seem dirty, they were just sharing, as good friends do.

They parted at the cross-roads with a promise to meet at the swing park in the morning, if the weather was fine.

* * *

The next day dawned bright and sunny, and Sylvia asked her mother if she could go to Goose Green. Mrs. Short readily agreed. They never went away on holidays as Mr. Short rarely took time off work apart from a couple of weeks which he normally spent redecorating the house.

Sylvia was delighted. She put on one of her summer frocks and hurried to the top of the road. Veronica was not there; in fact, the swing park had not been opened. That was no problem for Sylvia. Hitching up her frock, she clambered over the railings in order to jump down the other side. Unfortunately, she caught her frock on one of the spikes and it ripped as she jumped down. She decided that she couldn't very well stay there with the back of her frock hanging out and her knickers showing, so she slowly made her way back home, knowing only too well what her punishment would be. She told her mother tearfully that it was an accident.

"Accident or not, you have ruined a perfectly good frock with your stupid clumsiness and you know the punishment for that," said Mrs. Short grimly. "Take the frock off and get upstairs to bed."

Sylvia consoled herself with the thought that she had a couple of books to read, but she did wonder what Veronica would think, and whether she had gone to Goose Green to look for her.

She was allowed down in the evening for dinner and had to suffer more insults as her mother told her father what a naughty girl she had been.

After dinner she was obliged to go back upstairs and await further punishment.

She found that, as she was getting older, she could no longer escape as lightly as she had done in the past. Mr. Short now carried out his wife's instructions to the full. However the 'tickles' didn't stop and this time Sylvia found that she definitely didn't like what her father did to her. He came upstairs and beat her with the cane; then he made her lie down whilst he spread her legs apart, opened his trousers, lay on top of her and tried to push his long pink thing inside her. It hurt and she told him to stop; but he just laughed and carried on until, with a loud moan, he spent himself.

The next morning when Sylvia awoke, she noticed to her horror that there was blood all over the sheets. She got up quickly and went to the toilet, but she was too frightened to wee. She was convinced that she was dying as her insides felt torn apart. In the end she went and told her mother about it, and that she was bleeding 'down there'. To her amazement, she was not scolded; instead, Mrs. Short went to her own bedroom and came back with a big fat ugly-looking thing which reminded Sylvia of a hammock. She was told to put it inside her knickers and that she was a woman now and had to be more careful.

Sylvia, for the life of her, couldn't understand what all this was about. She wasn't a woman; she was only eleven. Sighing, she did what her mother told her and thought it was most uncomfortable and bulky. To make matters worse, Mrs. Short decided that after the incident with the torn frock she had better wear some ' sensible clothes', so today Sylvia found herself decked out in her brother's khaki shorts, long brown socks, an olive green T-shirt and brown sandals with a strap which went across the middle. She was almost ashamed to look at herself in the mirror, and she knew what the other children would say. But she was so desperate to meet her friend that she had to grin and bear it; she only hoped that not too many of the other girls and boys that she knew would be there.

"Where were you yesterday?" Veronica asked as soon as they met. "I waited over two hours before going back home."

Sylvia explained about ripping her frock and that she had been sent to bed.

It seemed a harsh form of punishment to Veronica for something so trivial, and she was glad that her own mother didn't treat her like that. She secretly thought that Mrs. Short was like the wicked stepmother in the story of Cinderella, and she wished she could take Sylvia home for her mother to look after. Then they could be friends for ever.

Veronica said that the school in Adys Road was running a summer play group – would Sylvia be allowed to join her there? Then they could do a lot

36

more things during the day. To Sylvia's surprise, Mrs. Short agreed to give it a trial, made some sandwiches for her, and even suggested that she stay there all day until it finished at five o' clock.

At nine o' clock the next morning, Sylvia met Veronica and they spent a lovely time at the school playing with all the toys. They even went rope climbing. The play-group had all sorts of wonderful games organised and there was even talk of going on a few picnics to Peckham Rye Park. Sylvia wasn't sure whether her mother would permit this, but she decided to ask anyway.

It was around lunchtime when she noticed that some of the other children were laughing and pointing at her, but she was so used to it that she didn't pay very much attention. Then, as she got up to get a drink of water from the fountain, Veronica noticed the patch of blood.

Grabbing Sylvia by the arm, she whispered: "Have you hurt your bum?"

"No," said Sylvia in bewilderment. "Why?"

"Look at the back of your shorts. They're covered in blood."

Sylvia glanced down to where she had been sitting and saw to her horror that there was blood everywhere. It had seeped through her shorts and stained the bench. She tried ineffectively to wipe it off with the greaseproof paper that her sandwiches were wrapped in.

"I'll go and tell Miss," said Veronica, hurrying off with an alarmed expression: she was afraid that her friend might be bleeding to death.

The helper came and took one look; then she went quickly to fetch a wet cloth. "I'll take you home to your mummy," she said.

Sylvia hastily bade her friend goodbye and followed the friendly helper out of the gate. Fortunately, their house was just around the corner and, with the helper's jumper discreetly placed around Sylvia's waist, they reached home without further mishap.

Sylvia had no idea what the woman said to her mother, but once indoors she was made to go to the bathroom to take off the soiled articles, before being given another uncomfortable 'hammock'. Mrs. Short offered no information and Sylvia didn't dare to ask how long she was expected to wear this bulky piece of material in her knickers; but the next day her mother told her to take another with her in her pocket and that if she felt wet she must put that on.

Of course it happened again, and Sylvia, not realising that she was to wear only one at a time, put the second one on top of the first one, which prevented her from walking properly. It also looked as if she was wearing a nappy. The other children were quick to notice and make fun of her. Luckily for Sylvia, the friendly helper was there again to offer advice.

"Didn't your mummy tell you what is happening to your body?" she asked.

Sylvia shook her head and shamefacedly looked down at her feet. The helper took her on one side and explained what all the blood was for and how long she might be expected to put up with it.

Sylvia didn't like the thought of having this happen once a month and asked whether she could stop it. The helper advised her about this, too, so that by the time Sylvia went home she felt much happier; at least she knew now that she wasn't going to die from a rare blood disorder.

It was obvious that her mother was too embarrassed to discuss such subjects. She must have spoken Mr. Short, however, because he told Sylvia that they must be more careful now that she was growing up and had 'the curse'. Sylvia thought that it was called 'month-lies', but it was still all very mysterious to her. She confided in Veronica, but her friend confessed that she didn't know anything about it. Sylvia then thought that she must be very special indeed to have such a thing happen to her, and she really began to feel grown up.

Chapter Four

Towards the end of the summer holidays, Mrs. Short took Sylvia to the school outfitters at Grove Vale to get her rigged out for her new school. They bought a navy blue blazer, two navy blue cardigans, a navy blue beret and finally two badges with a golden eagle on them. Sylvia thought it was wonderful. She had never had a uniform before. From the arcade in Rye Lane, her mother purchased some lengths of gingham in blue and red, thinking that she would save money by making her daughter's frocks.

The first morning of the September term, Sylvia was up early, hardly able to contain her excitement. She and her friend June would be going to school together.

Originally, June's mother had been going to accompany them, but they had protested that it was a babyish thing to do and that none of the other girls would be taken to school by their parents. After a heated discussion, they were allowed to go by themselves.

June called at the house, and Sylvia was immediately concerned to find that, although June was wearing the same colour frock, the check on hers was noticeably smaller. As they began the rather long walk to school, June explained that her mother had bought her frocks from the shop at Grove Vale, along with the other bits and pieces.

Sylvia hoped that the other girls wouldn't comment too much, but that hope flew out of the window when they reached the school playground. Some of the older girls, who had been there for a couple of years, broke off talking together, as soon as they saw Sylvia, and started to laugh. She found that she was the only pupil at the school with a frock in a check that size. She felt so humiliated that she wanted to turn round and run back home again.

"Well, look what we have here," said a tall, spotty girl with long lanky hair.

"Who needs a draught-board when you've got a frock like that!" said another, who was smaller but much prettier.

"Come on," said June, tucking her arm comfortably under Sylvia's. "Don't let them see you're bothered by it; they'll only pick on you all the more."

The whistle blew and the new girls had to line up on

one side of the playground. Sylvia wished she hadn't worn her beret as none of the bigger girls were wearing theirs. Even June had taken hers off. It was too late to do anything about it now, but she made a mental note to take it off before she got into school the next day.

They were allotted classrooms and teachers. Sylvia found out that her teacher was called Miss Simpson, and that she would be in class 1A. June was called to Class 1C which was disappointing, for they had both hoped to be together. The whistle went again and the pupils trooped into their respective classrooms and were told to sit down at the desks. Sylvia plumped for one at the back thinking that, that way, there was less chance of her being picked on. Some of the girls already knew each other and were pairing off, but Sylvia didn't recognise any of them. She was wondering who was going to sit next to her, when a big fat girl breezed in and squeezed into the seat beside her. She looked friendly enough, but it was too early to tell.

The teacher rapped on the desk with a ruler. "I shall be calling the class register," she announced, "and when I do, will you please stand up one by one as your name is called and say: 'Present, Miss Simpson'."

Sylvia looked around the classroom and counted twenty-six pupils, including herself. Miss Simpson had a slight accent, but it was difficult to make out what it was. She was a woman of medium height and build, with very dark hair pleated into a French roll fastened neatly at the back of her head. She had a swarthy complexion, with huge brown eyes, and wore large black-framed spectacles which, when not in use, dangled from her neck on a chain. She had a pointed nose and even white teeth and looked about the same age as Sylvia's mother.

The roll call began and each girl rose obediently when her turn came. They all looked friendly enough, and Sylvia desperately hoped that this would be the case.

When her name was called, she too stood up and acknowledged Miss Simpson. She felt that everybody was looking at her in her horrid check dress. She replied quickly and, blushing, sat down. She had noticed a couple of the other girls whispering and nudging each other.

"Don't worry," whispered 'fat girl' confidentially. "I hate the first day at a new school. Perhaps you and I will become friends."

Sylvia sincerely hoped not, as she didn't think that she liked this girl very much. It had nothing to do with the fact that she was overweight. But she looked sly and had piggy eyes. Her hair was lank and unkempt and she also had big spots all over her forehead.

She found out at playtime that the fat girl's name was Geraldine Harper. Geraldine persisted in following her everywhere she went. She placed an arm around Sylvia's shoulders possessively, and led her into a quiet corner before pointing out various girls that she had known from her old school. She then proceeded to repeat gossip about each of them. Sylvia didn't like this much and it made her wary of telling Geraldine anything about herself. She missed Veronica and wished she could be there.

She was relieved when she noticed June hurrying towards her. Making some excuse, she hastily went to join her.

"Who's your friend?" giggled June.

"She's not my friend!" retorted Sylvia angrily. "She annoys me. I can't go anywhere without her following me. Anyway, forget about her; how are you getting on in your class?"

"Well, not too bad. I feel a bit strange, but most of the other girls are nice. I still wish we'd been put together."

"Never mind, it'll get better; and at least we still have each other to walk home with."

* * *

By the start of the second term, Sylvia was pleasantly surprised to find that she was one of the most popular girls in her class. She had been chosen by the rest of the form to be their prefect, a high honour indeed! Geraldine had latched onto another unsuspecting victim, leaving the way clear for Sylvia to make friends with some of the others. A vivacious, bubbly, red-haired girl called Georgina became a special favourite. She and Sylvia vied with each other for top place in the form. It became a contest between them, and the rest of the class used to place bets with anything available (mainly sweets) in the hope that their particular friend would win.

Sylvia excelled at English; it was all that really interested her. She actually loathed needlework. She had been trying to make an apron, but it had been unpicked so many times that it was now practically falling to bits. History was boring, and she didn't understand Geography. She could scrape by in Maths and the Cookery lessons could be fun. She was simply indifferent about all the other subjects.

Christmas was fast approaching and she had volunteered to produce and act in the school pantomime. It was a skit on Cinderella. Geraldine and one of her new cronies were chosen to play the two ugly sisters. Georgina was Cinderella and Sylvia was Prince Charming. Sylvia didn't want anyone to feel left out so she invented lots of other characters so that all of Class 1A could be included. Geraldine made herself jump when the balloon she had stuffed up her cardigan to make herself look even fatter, suddenly burst.

The parents and staff alike thought the evening a great success. The Headmistress, Miss Conway, had a very soft spot for Sylvia, whom she now thought of as her protege. She had high hopes for her, knowing that she had it in her one day to go to university. She had been the brunt of many school jokes herself and recently had caught Sylvia standing up in the assembly hall doing a very good impersonation of her, to the delight of the other girls. To her credit, she wasn't cross in the least.

* * *

It was embarrassing for Sylvia. "I haven't got you one," she said for the umpteenth time as she

45

unwrapped yet another present. It seemed that all the girls in her class had bought her something, from tins of toffee to cheap bath cubes and soap. She had never had so many presents before. She had tried asking for some extra pocket money at home as the threepence which she normally received was quite inadequate. Her father had left her alone lately, which was quite a welcome relief, although it did mean that she lost out on an extra threepence on the odd occasions.

The girls all assured her that it didn't matter; but it did to Sylvia.

Christmas brought with it the usual illnesses. This year she went down with tonsillitis and swollen glands. Her throat was so sore that she couldn't swallow properly. Then it developed into 'flu. Her mother massaged camphorated oil on her chest and put oil of eucalyptus on her hankie. She had also got an itchy bottom and to her horror she discovered tiny white threads wiggling around in her 'number two's'. She told her mother and the very next day the district nurse came in and put a tube in her bottom and poured some soapy water down it. It hurt a bit, but it must have done the trick for after three visits she noticed that the wiggly white threads had now disappeared.

Every Friday evening before going to bed, her mother would make up a cup of liquorice powder which Sylvia was obliged to drink, though it made her retch. The powder was placed in half a cup of warm water, then stirred. She would watch in fascination when a large bubble appeared on the surface. She poked it with her finger and the bubble dispersed, leaving powder floating on the surface. The liquorice powder was meant to clean your bowels out; taking it was as much of a ritual as going to the lavvy each day when you didn't want to. Her mother was quite fanatical about such things and it was pointless to argue with her.

Chapter Five

In July, 1956, Sylvia had been at Friern for nearly a year. The school holidays were coming up and she had received an excellent report. Her parents were pleased with her and told her so, which made her feel good. She resolved to do even better next term.

Despite her home environment, Sylvia was essentially a happy girl and a 'game little trier'. Her father against his better judgement, and no doubt to please his wife, had now bought a television set. They had a bit more money coming in these days, because Mrs. Short had advertised for a lodger. Mr. Cohen was his name, and Sylvia didn't like him. He had her grandmother's old bedroom, but he used the bathroom next door to Sylvia's bedroom. She tried to avoid him, but it wasn't always possible. After dinner, he would linger downstairs and offer to help with the washing up. Mrs. Short was much taken with him; Sylvia thought the word was 'refined'. Now as he sat watching the television, he told Sylvia to come and sit on his lap. She would be twelve in a few months and thought she was a bit too old for that. Not being used to affection, she didn't know how to handle it.

Her mother, overhearing, encouraged her to do as he asked; she didn't want to offend her lodger. He paid good money and she was determined to do everything in her power to make him happy.

So Sylvia obeyed and sat on his lap, not daring to move. Nothing untoward happened; he just kept telling her what a pretty girl she was and that he would wait for her to grow up so that they could get married. She thought he was the ugliest man she had ever seen. He had hardly any hair, his nose was like a beak and the worst thing was that his breath smelt foul.

She watched the television for some time and then a programme came on and, for the first time, she was in love. It was about Robin Hood and starred an actor called Richard Greene. He was so brave and handsome that she sat there spellbound for the next half an hour. When she saw June the next day they discussed the programme, and both decided they were in love. Sylvia had fallen for Rock Hudson, Stewart Grainger and Alan Ladd before, but she had never felt like this. It was decided that as she was better at writing letters, she should write to Richard and tell him that he had two people in love with him and what was he going to do about it. He would have to choose between them. Sylvia was sure he would pick June, because there was no doubt that she was much prettier than her. She didn't have teeth that stuck out; hers were nice and white and even.

The next time Robin Hood came on television, she managed to note the address of the studios where it was being filmed. When she went to bed that night, she wrote the letter, declaring her undying love. She decided to omit all mention of June, just in case . . .

A week later a letter came addressed to her. Her mother quickly opened it despite Sylvia's protests.

"No secrets in this house, my girl," she was told firmly.

Inside the letter was a lovely photograph signed by Richard Greene. To Sylvia's disappointment, he did not reciprocate her passionate declaration.

On the way to school, she showed June the photograph.

"Ooh!" breathed June. "You lucky devil! Didn't you tell him I love him as well? Why did he only send you a photograph and not me?"

This put Sylvia in rather a hole. She could hardly admit that she hadn't mentioned her at all, so she made some excuse and hoped that June would forget all about it.

It was a fine day, and when they reached school Miss Simpson suggested that they all go over to Peckham Rye Park to do a nature study lesson. The girls were thrilled to get out of the classroom and have a chance to lark around.

They spent the morning identifying trees and plants and picking up various leaves to take back to look at under the microscope.

On the way back to school, some of the girls started pointing, and when Sylvia looked to see what had taken their attention, she noticed caravans of every shape and size and realised that the fair had come. She had never been to the fair before, but could remember hearing the music one evening a year earlier as she sat in her bedroom.

Gloria Jones wanted Sylvia to go with her and her sister one evening. Gloria lived in Anstey Road and was the youngest of a family of seven children. Her father and two eldest brothers had a rather dubious reputation – mainly for getting drunk, fighting and stealing. Sylvia had visited the house without her mother knowing and thought her parents had been extremely nice. Gloria explained that they had originally come from Wales, which must account for Gloria's mother's lilting voice.

"I'll ask my mum," said Sylvia dubiously, "but I don't think she will let me go." She knew full well that her mother didn't approve of the Jones' family; and that she was even more deeply prejudiced against the fair.

During the dinner break, some of the other girls in Sylvia's class said they were going to have a look at the fair. Sylvia was invited to join them. She hesitated momentarily, because she had some revision to do. Damn the revision, she thought.

They got to the site just in time to see some of the

men putting the rides together, muscles rippling under the strain of the big metal poles. Tents were being pitched, ready for the side shows. Buckets and buckets of goldfish were swimming around, waiting to be given out as prizes to those lucky people who could win one by picking a lucky number in a straw.

The girls wandered around fascinated by all they saw. Suddenly, a boy of about fifteen came into view behind one of the caravans.

"He's mine!" Gloria stated firmly. "I saw him first."

"You can have him," said some of the others. "We wouldn't be seen dead with a 'gippo'."

But the boy only had eyes for Sylvia. He smiled at her, his white teeth gleaming in the sunlight. He was several inches taller than she was, and had black hair which curled over his collar. His complexion was swarthy and his eyes were dark brown, framed by long thick lashes. He walked boldly up to Sylvia and asked her name.

She was taken aback at this. She had never had a boy interested in her before. She had so little confidence in herself that she didn't realise that the older she got, the more attractive she became. She was very slim, with long dark hair cut in a fringe across her forehead. Her eyes which were green and expressive, were her best feature.

"Why, you cheeky boy! I don't think I want to tell you!" she retorted, trying to look cross.

"Please yourself then." He walked off jauntily, whistling, leaving half the class of 1A swooning.

"What's wrong with you?" cried Gloria. "He's

smashing! Cor, I wish he'd asked me out; I'd have gone like a shot!"

"There's nothing wrong with me. I'm too busy to be interested in cheeky boys." Sylvia followed the others back to school, thinking about the boy and wishing now that she had asked his name at least. Still, she doubted that she would see him again.

They finished school early that afternoon because some of the classes had a free period. As she and June were walking home, Sylvia spotted Gloria and a girl called Maureen going into Hudson's shop at the top of East Dulwich Road. Then they came out and slipped round the corner. When they reappeared, they were smoking a cigarette.

"Do you want a quick puff?" asked Gloria casually, blowing the smoke out of her nostrils like a dragon.

June flatly refused to have anything to do with it. This was partly because of her asthma, and partly because she thought it a dirty habit and she didn't like the smell of smoke. Sylvia on the other hand was curious.

"I'll try it for a laugh," she said, reaching out to take the smoking cigarette. She placed the end of it in her mouth and took a puff before blowing it out again.

"No! You don't do it like that, do it like this." Maureen placed the cigarette between her lips, took a long pull and inhaled deeply. Then she blew the smoke slowly out through her mouth and nose. "Here, you try it now."

Sylvia copied her friend. Suddenly she felt the ground rushing up to meet her. She broke out in a cold sweat and was sure her face had gone green. Her head was swimming; it was ghastly.

"Don't worry about it; it's always bad the first time. You'll get used to it," Gloria said with a laugh. "We always come in here to buy our cigarettes. They're not supposed to sell them to children, but we tell them they're for our parents. It's better when we have enough money for five or even ten, but today we could only afford a penny Woodbine and they got a bit suspicious."

Sylvia wasn't at all sure that she liked smoking, but she did confess that it made her feel grown up. June had gone all huffy and wasn't speaking to her. So they walked the rest of the way home in silence, having left Gloria and Maureen at the corner of Gowlett Road.

"Why did you have to do that?" June burst out suddenly. "Did it make you feel important? I could shake you sometimes. You know your mother doesn't like you hanging around with Gloria. She'll get you into trouble one of these days!"

"Oh, shut up!" retorted Sylvia. "I can do what I like; I don't have to have you telling me all the time. I happen to like Gloria and Maureen, so there!"

Striding away from her friend, she turned towards her house and, putting her hand through the letter box, pulled out the string with the front door key on the end. She turned the key in the lock, opened the door and swung around to give June a final glare before poking her tongue out and going inside.

"I hate her," she said to no-one in particular; but she didn't really mean it.

The house was quiet. That in itself was unusual. Surely her mother couldn't be out? A low moaning noise came from upstairs. It sounded as if someone was in pain. What if her mother had tripped and hurt herself? Warned by some sixth sense not to call out, she crept quietly up the stairs. The noise came again, and from the direction of her parents' bedroom. Peering through the door Sylvia was shocked to see that her mother was not alone. Mr. Cohen was there in bed with her, and he was jumping up and down on top of her and saying all sorts of naughty words. Her mother was tossing and turning her head and making groaning noises. Sylvia didn't know what to do. Should she say something? What on earth was happening? Was Mr. Cohen hurting her mother? She wished her father was here. He would know what to do. In the end, she decided to beat a hasty retreat. She crept silently back down the stairs and out into the street.

"What is it?" cried June as she opened her front door. "You look terrible! I bet it was that cigarette you had. Come upstairs, we can talk in private then."

"It's my mother and Mr. Cohen."

"Yes! Well what about them?"

"I think he may be hurting her. She keeps moaning and making funny noises. He's jumping up and down on top of her."

"What, like this?" June demonstrated on top of the bed.

"Yes, that's it."

"Oh, I wouldn't worry about that, he's only telling

her how much he loves her. Mum and Dad have pretend fights sometimes, especially when they don't know I'm watching."

"But Dad loves her, too, and he saw her first! I don't want Mr. Cohen to love her."

"I shouldn't tell your Dad if I were you," June said wisely.

"No, I shan't. I won't say anything to anyone. I'll just pretend it didn't happen."

At that moment June's mother, Mrs. Johnson, came bustling into the bedroom. Seeing their faces, she said: "What is it? Girlie secrets? Don't worry, I'm not listening. I only came to see if you wanted anything to drink. Tea or coffee, take your pick."

Sylvia had not tasted coffee before. Her mother had said it was too expensive when her father had asked why they couldn't have some for a change.

"Yes, please," she said, trying to look self-assured. "I would like a cup of coffee."

Winnie Johnson smiled. "All right then. Give me five minutes and then come down to the kitchen. You know what I said about food and drink in the bedroom . . ."

"Yes, Mum, I know. I'm not allowed to encourage mice in the house." June pulled a face as her mother went downstairs.

"Have you got any mice?" asked Sylvia excitedly. "I have. They're in my toy box in the bedroom and they make scratching noises at night. Once I got up and I couldn't switch the light on to see them because mother had taken the light bulb out."

"Whatever for?"

"She said I was wasting electricity by reading in bed, so she took the bulb out."

"That's a mean thing to do!"

"Anyway, I knew it was mice because the next day I found some pieces of cardboard and paper which had been chewed up really small."

June shivered, pulling her cardigan around her shoulders. "Aren't you scared?" she said. "They give me the creeps."

"No! How can you be scared of a little mouse? It won't hurt you. It's more frightened of you. Why, we must look like big giants to them! Come on, I want to try some of your mum's coffee."

"There you are, then," said Mrs. Johnson, placing the steaming cup in front of her.

Sylvia thought what a luxury it was, and how grown up she felt. She stared at the top where a skin had now formed.

"I haven't put any sugar in it. Perhaps you'd like to try it without."

It didn't taste very nice without sugar, so Sylvia helped herself to one teaspoonful. Stirring it briskly, she watched as the skin disappeared into the milky liquid. Tentatively, she took her first sip. It was nice, very nice.

"I like it, I really do," she stated categorically, smacking her lips in satisfaction.

"That's good," beamed Mrs. Johnson. "By the way, I've been meaning to ask your mother if she'll let you have June's old gramophone. Only, you see, I've bought her a new one and her father was going to throw the old one out. There's nothing wrong with it; it still plays. It's just that it's a bit old."

"Could you ask her for me, please? It'll sound better coming from you."

"Of course I will. I'll pop round now, shall I?"

"No. Not now. Later will do," replied Sylvia, a little too quickly, thinking of her mother and Mr. Cohen being caught unawares.

She drank her coffee with relish and then made her way next door, hoping that things were back to normal. She found her mother busying herself in the kitchen.

"You're home early," Mrs. Short remarked. "Go and get changed, and then you can play next door until your meal is ready".

Sylvia obeyed complacently, not daring to say that that was where she had just come from.

Later on that evening, Mrs. Johnson knocked on the door. Her mother went to answer it and then came back to confer with Mr. Short. Sylvia couldn't hear what was said, but the next minute she saw her father carrying the old gramophone up to her bedroom.

"You'll have to look after it," he warned. "And buy your own records and needles."

"Oh, I will!" breathed Sylvia in delight, hardly able to contain her excitement.

She ran upstairs to look at this wonder. There were so many records she wanted to buy. She used to listen to Radio Luxembourg on her brother's crystal set in the evenings. Sometimes the interference and crackling was really bad, but she could make out some of the songs that were being played. The only other chance she got to hear the latest music was on 'Children's Choice' with Uncle Mac and 'Family Favourites' at Sunday lunch time. The B.B.C. offered a choice of two stations, the Home Service and the Light Programme. Till recently she had liked listening to 'Educating Archie', 'Life with the Lyons', 'Take it from Here', and the Billy Cotton Band Show.

The girls at school were all talking about a new rock star called Elvis Presley. She had heard his record on Radio Luxembourg, but preferred a singer by the name of Pat Boone. She had a picture of him taken from a packet of bubble gum, and she thought he was very handsome. Elvis, on the other hand, looked mean. Sylvia didn't like the way he wore his hair, which was black and greasy; Pat Boone was more clean cut.

Tomorrow she would go to the record shop and buy a box of needles, which cost one penny. Maybe she would have enough money at the weekend to buy a record. She knew exactly which one she wanted. She had heard it on the wireless and it was played on her favourite television programme. It was by someone called Dick James, and was the theme from 'Robin Hood'. If she saved her money and went without sweets and her dinner, she could just about afford it.

What an eventful day! Coffee and a gramophone! The episode of her mother and Mr. Cohen was forgotten in the excitement.

Chapter Six

"I'll let you have a go if you like," said Gloria, stepping off the bicycle. "It's really easy."

"I don't know." Sylvia looked at the bike doubtfully. "It's a long way to fall off."

"Look, I'll hold onto you; you'll be as safe as houses. Come on – or are you scared?"

"I'm not scared of anything." With that she sprang up onto the saddle and, wobbling precariously, set off along the road with Gloria in close pursuit trying to desperately to steady her friend. In the end she had to let go and Sylvia began pedalling frantically. Next minute she ended up in an uncompromising heap on the ground, her legs stuck up, unladylike, in the air. They fell about laughing.

"I don't think I'm any good at this," said Sylvia, ruefully rubbing a bruised shin.

"You'll get better if you keep practising. You can borrow it any time you like."

Sylvia nodded. "My mother has got a part time job now, so I can practise after school."

Her mother's job, at the local sweet shop in Amott Road, had given Sylvia a lot more freedom. She had discovered the thrill of riding down Dog Kennel Hill on a skate. What you did was to put a book on the skate and sit on the book while you went hurtling down the hill. The only thing that was not so good was that once you reached the bottom, you had to walk all the way up to the top of the hill to start all over again. However, it was great fun and she also loved going to Peckham Rye and playing in what was called the 'Dog Pond'. The game was to jump from the edge to reach the drain in the middle without falling in. The water was dirty and had dead fish floating on the top. Mrs. Short would have been horrified if she had known the number of occasions that Sylvia had come home soaking wet from a dunking in the pond! Long legs were not one of Sylvia's strongest points and you definitely needed long legs to clear the pond.

Today when she let herself indoors, she rushed straight up to the bathroom and was violently sick. She had been feeling off-colour for several days and her tummy was slightly swollen. She thought she must be due for the 'curse' as she hadn't had one for a few months. She had learnt in the biology lesson at school that, for the first few years, periods in teenagers can be irregular and were nothing to worry about.

She got undressed and looked at herself in the mirror. Ugly blue veins ran from her neck down along her breasts, which looked swollen. Her tummy was larger than normal and she had a dull ache in the pit of her stomach. And there was something else that bothered her: her head was constantly itching. She took her hairbrush and began to brush her hair vigorously over the white surface of the boiler. On closer inspection she noticed tiny grey specks moving among her loose hair; they looked like dirty coloured dandruff. She decided to keep them there until Mrs. Short came in from work and could tell her what they were.

Changing out of her school uniform, she set about peeling the potatoes for the evening meal. Now that her mother was at work, Sylvia seemed to be doing most of the household chores. John was no help: he would come home from school, get changed and then disappear into his bedroom with the door shut. She had no idea what he was doing in there; once she had asked him to help her prepare the dinner and all she had got was a kick. In his opinion, it was women's work and that was that! She sighed wistfully as she wished once again that she had been born a boy.

When her mother came home at five o' clock, she was pleased to see that the potatoes were already on the stove and boiling away merrily.

"Can you come up to the bathroom?" asked Sylvia. "I've got something to show you."

Her mother went with her to examine the top of the boiler.

"I should think you must have walked under a tree and they dropped on your head," she said. "Don't worry about it."

Sylvia accepted her mother's explanation without question.

At school the next day, the nurse was doing the first of her twice yearly rounds. Sylvia queued up with the others outside the headmistress's office. When it was her turn to go in, she was told to take off her shoes and socks. The nurse looked at her arches and said they were fine. Next she got a metal comb and placed it in some disinfectant before running it through Sylvia's hair. When she had finished she gave a self-satisfied smile and wrote out a note, which she enclosed in an envelope for Sylvia to take home to her mother. Then, noticing that the girl looked peaky, she asked if there was anything she wanted to ask while she was there.

"Well," said Sylvia, "I do feel sick a lot of the time, and I haven't had a period for several months."

"How old are you now?"

"I'll be fourteen in five months time."

"Roll up your sleeve; I'll take your blood pressure while I'm here." This was done and all seemed to be in order. Next the nurse asked if she had any pains.

"Yes, in my stomach," Sylvia replied. "They keep me awake sometimes."

The nurse made her get up onto the couch, and

63

gave her an examination. When the nurse had finished, she told her to get dressed while she turned
away and wrote some notes.

"What is it? What's wrong with me?" asked Sylvia,
who was close to tears. She didn't know what was happening to her.

"Well, my dear, I can't be sure, but I think you're
going to have a baby," replied the nurse gently.

Sylvia was shocked. How on earth did it happen?
She didn't know much about having babies or how
they got there; it was something they had yet to cover
in the biology lesson. Some of the girls whom she had
overheard talking about it, said that they came out of
your body through a beauty spot. She had rather a
large one on the back of her leg so she guessed that was
the place to look. She said as much to the nurse, who
laughed sadly and then shook her head.

"I wish they'd teach you more about the facts of life
at school so that you girls wouldn't be so ignorant
about it," she sighed. "Look, I'll book you an appointment with your doctor to confirm it, as I could be
wrong. Your parents will also have to be told."

Sylvia felt her heart sink. This was awful! It was a
sin to have a baby when you weren't even married.
She had overheard her mother telling her father one
day about a neighbour who wasn't married and whose
baby was black. The neighbour, at nineteen, was quite
a bit older than her. She had been sent to a home in the
country when the baby was due, and when she came
back she had received threats from people living
around her. Her parents had decided to move away

and make a fresh start somewhere; the last she had heard was that they were going to live in a place called the Bronx in New York.

* * *

Mrs. Short read the note from the nurse and then tore it into small pieces.

"Nits! She says the child has got nits! How can she have with hair as clean as that!"

She grabbed Sylvia by the neck and thrust her head into a bowl of cold water, at the same time vigorously scrubbing shampoo into her scalp.

"You're hurting me!" protested Sylvia loudly.

"Hurt you! You don't know the meaning of the word. It's mixing with those dirty girls at school. I told you I didn't want you playing with them!" She took some paraffin and proceeded to rub it into Sylvia's hair. "You'll have to leave this on for a week before we even think about washing it again."

Sylvia thought she would die of shame. It smelt to high heaven and she knew she would be the laughing stock of the school. Arguing with her mother about anything was useless; if she tried, she would normally end up being punished further. She kept quiet. Luckily, the nurse hadn't contacted her mother with the other news. She hoped that if she didn't think about the baby, it would go away.

Now she was being sent to bed to await further punishment from her father and all because she had nits. It was unfair! She didn't do these things deliberately.

While she was waiting she reflected on the day a couple of months ago when she had had sixpence pocket money. It was coming up to Mothers' Day and she had seen some lovely daffodils which she thought her mother would like. She had spent all her money on them and walked proudly home with them wrapped in pretty paper. When she had presented them to Mrs. Short, she had taken them and broken the stems in half before putting them in the dustbin.

"I don't need your presents!" she had said fiercely. "It's the sign of a guilty conscience. You're not my child, anyway. Your own mother didn't want you, and I'm not surprised. If only she could see how ugly you've become! You're like a worm that has crawled up out of the ground!"

Stunned by this sudden and unprovoked attack, Sylvia had run to her room, crying. When she had recovered sufficiently to be able to bring herself to look at her reflection in the mirror, she felt she had to agree with her mother. Her teeth stuck out badly and she felt that no boy would ever want to kiss her. She puckered up her lips to kiss her reflection in the mirror and her teeth clanged against the glass. It was no good, she would never be pretty like some of her friends, who already had boy-friends.

Her stomach churned as she heard her father's footsteps on the stairs. He was becoming less discreet about their little 'tickles' now, and he frightened her with his demands. He had postponed the punishment session until his wife had gone next door to Mrs. Johnson's and John had gone to his Sea Scouts meeting. He knew there was no-one in to hear her cries of protest.

"Hello, my darling!" he said, stepping into the bedroom. "Are you still awake to show Daddy how much you love him?"

Sylvia nodded mutely as she watched her father take off all his clothes. She lay on the bed, too frightened to move as he joined her under the covers. He began by kissing her on the mouth. His kisses were wet and slobbery and Sylvia didn't like him doing that. He pulled the covers back to look at her body which was now beginning to show signs of womanhood.

"My word, look at these!" he said, bending his mouth down to suckle at her breasts. "They're getting big."

Sylvia was conscious of her body hair. She had a few hairs under her arms and a lot on her 'muff'. It embarrassed her, but she knew that most of the girls in her class were in the same state. She had seen them when they got changed in the showers after swimming, and Georgina had bright red tufts under her arms, so she guessed that it must be normal. She waited for her father to get on top of her, but to her distress he turned her over and entered her from behind. She felt a sharp pain in her bottom which got worse with his thrusts. She tried to turn over, but he had her pinned down firmly with his legs.

"Please stop it," she moaned. "You're hurting me."

"No, darling, Daddy's not hurting you. You like it. I know you do. Let me show you how much I love you. Your mummy doesn't show she loves me. She's cold.

You're so warm and young and innocent."

The thrusting seemed to go on forever and the pain in her bottom grew more intense. Sylvia thought she was going to burst. Suddenly, thankfully, it was all over and he got up and began to get dressed. Sylvia was left sobbing.

She thought she couldn't stand much more of this; one day soon she was going to run away. She had a bottle by the bedroom door where she used to keep any spare pennies. She would count that and see how much she had got. She had no idea where to go, but at the moment she didn't care. Perhaps she would find her real mother. She didn't believe that a mother couldn't care for her own child. When they were together again, everything would be all right – but how to find her? Where would she start?

She fell into a troubled sleep, and dreamt about goblins attacking her in the bedroom; then she got up to put the light on, but that didn't work. In the early hours of the morning she woke up perspiring and with her heart thumping. Her body felt sore. Perhaps she should tell her mother about her father. Maybe she could do something to help.

Chapter Seven

The next morning she looked in the mirror and noticed that her eyes were swollen up. She quickly splashed some cold water onto her face and went downstairs to breakfast. Luckily her father had already left for work. She didn't think she could face him after last night's episode. She could tell that her mother was happy because she was humming a little tune under her breath while she buttered the bread in the scullery. She didn't feel like having anything to eat, so she took a quick drink of milk out of the jug and made some excuse to leave the table.

June was just coming up the path as she opened the door, and the two friends hurried to the top of the road where they had arranged to meet Gloria and Maureen.

They had got into the habit, if they were early for school, of paying a visit to Fred's Cafe on the corner, where they could go in and play the juke box. Fred never minded if they didn't have the money to buy a coffee. He looked forward to seeing them and to listening to their cheery banter. The four of them arrived at eight-thirty.

"I've got a shilling," stated June.

"Good-oh!" they all chorused. "We can play two records for that."

Each of them had different tastes in music. Left to herself, Sylvia would have chosen 'April Love' by Pat Boone, or 'Catch a Falling Star' by Perry Como. Maureen wanted to hear Elvis singing 'Wear My Ring Around Your Neck'. Gloria, however liked Tommy Steele singing 'Nairobi', and June said she would like 'Kewpie Doll' by Frankie Vaughan and 'Stairway of Love' by Michael Holliday. It was decided that as they couldn't listen to them all at once, they should play two now and leave the others until later on in the week. That way they would all have a chance to hear their favourites.

"One day, Fred, we'll have a lot of money and we can come in and have a cooked breakfast," they said.

"That'll be the day!" he laughed, waving to them as they left. "You mind the roads now, and go careful."

"We will. 'Bye, Fred."

The bus strike was now in it's sixth week and the roads were comparatively clear. This morning they had to go to Ivydale School for the domestic science lessons, and it was a long walk. The previous week,

Gloria and Maureen had brought along a spare pair of roller skates and had painstakingly gone through the motions of teaching Sylvia how to ride on them. She had given up after five minutes, so now they pulled her along between them. It was a long arduous task, but better than walking, which would have taken them ages. They left June at the corner by Peckham Rye Common before proceeding up Nunhead Lane and turning left into Brockley Footpath, which led through the cemetery to Ivydale Road. Nunhead Cemetery was a creepy place and they took it in turns trying to scare each other; but today Sylvia failed to join in. They asked her what was the matter and Sylvia would dearly have wished to confide in them, but she remembered a promise she had made to her father, never to tell anyone else or something nasty would happen to her. She supposed that was another good reason for not confiding in her mother.

Later that day, on their return to Friern, they noticed a procession of caravans heading for Peckham Rye Park. The annual fair had come round again. It was too late to go and have a look now, but perhaps after school . . .

* * *

"Sylvia Short! Come out here and let's see what you have been doing this history lesson!"

Sylvia stood up and went to the front of the class. The other girls giggled and the giggling grew louder when Miss Simpson made her turn round to face them, for there on her forehead was a great black bubble. Sylvia had been given some chewing gum by one of her friends and, after chewing it until it grew soft, she had blown a big bubble and stuck it on her forehead, pretending it was a miner's lamp. The rest of the chewing gum was stuck on her teeth, which made it look as if she did not have any.

"Show me what you are hiding in your hand," boomed the teacher.

Reluctantly, Sylvia brought her hand from behind her back and opened it to reveal the tightly crumpled paper. The teacher unscrewed it.

"Well," she said, "I think the class can judge what a good little poet we have here. Read it out nice and loud."

Sylvia could feel herself blushing as she read the poem she had written:

> "I have a lover, his name is Richard Greene,
> He is tall, dark and handsome, and the bravest
>   man I've seen.
> His eyes are cornflower blue,
> His lips a pinky shade,
> He plays the part of Robin Hood
> a-wooing in the glade."

"Right! That's enough. You can stay behind and write out one hundred times, I MUST PAY ATTENTION IN CLASS."

Sylvia's heart sank. It meant that she wouldn't be able to join the others when they went to the fair.

"That's rotten luck," said June, when Sylvia told

her not to wait for her after school. "If you get it done quickly, we can meet you over there."

Sylvia glanced at the clock. It was four-thirty and she had nearly finished. She wondered if the others would really wait. She hurried along the corridor to the washroom and tried ineffectively to rub the chewing gum off her forehead. It had caught in her hair. Slipping into the needlework room, she rummaged around for a pair of scissors, with which she cut off a large lock of her hair and half an eyebrow in the process. She examined her reflection in the mirror. God! She did look strange! She hoped she could get away without drawing too much attention to herself.

"All right, Sylvia," said Miss Simpson. "You can go now and don't let me catch you doing anything as stupid again. I'm surprised at you. I gave you credit for more common sense."

Sylvia breathed a sigh of relief and set off hotfoot for the park. Her friends were nowhere to be seen. They must have gone.

As she turned to walk away, she felt a hand on her shoulder. She spun round and saw that it was the 'cheeky boy'. He had grown in the two years since she had last seen him, and he was as good-looking as ever.

"Hello, I'm Danny," he smiled, showing off his even set of white teeth. "I bumped into your friends; they said I might be lucky enough to see you later."

Sylvia felt herself blushing. "I'm Sylvia," she said hesitantly, unsure of how to react in this situation.

"Well, Sylvia, would you like me to show you around?"

"Yes, but not right now. I'm already late and my mother will be cross."

"When then?" the boy persisted.

"Tomorrow, after school?"

"Right then, it's a deal." He held out his hand, but spat on it first before shaking hands with Sylvia. Noticing her look, he said: "It's an old Romany way of sealing a pact. Now I know you won't break your promise."

Sylvia could feel his eyes burning into her back as she turned and walked away. She reached the house and was relieved to see that her mother wasn't yet home. On the mantelpiece there was a letter addressed to her mother in what looked like Mr. Cohen's handwriting. She replaced it before going into the scullery to prepare the vegetables for dinner.

"There's a good girl," puffed Mrs. Short as she eased her swollen ankles out of her shoes. "I'm really tired today. All this standing is making my feet ache. I've told him at the shop that I don't know how much longer I can keep this job up, and do you know what he said? He said there are plenty more who would be glad of the job if I don't want it. I nearly told him where to put it."

"Never mind," said Sylvia, sympathising with her mother and at the same time reflecting that that was possibly the longest conversation they had ever had. "There's a letter for you on the mantelpiece." She watched her mother's face turn white as she tore it open. "Is everything all right?"

"It's Mr. Cohen. He has to go back up north and he's not sure when or if he'll be coming back."

Mrs. Short soon recovered her self-control. Sylvia said nothing. She didn't like him anyway. Good riddance to bad rubbish!

"By the way," her mother continued, "I saw Doctor Saul today and he asked me to tell you to make an appointment to go and see him as soon as possible. He declined to tell me what it was all about. That's a bit rich. I am your mother, after all!"

Yes, thought Sylvia, and nosey with it!

"Okay," she replied aloud, "I'll go and see him tomorrow. I have a free study period in the morning."

"What's it all about?" queried Mrs. Short.

"Oh, nothing! I've just been a bit off colour lately." Sylvia was pleased that her mother's attention had been sufficiently distracted by Mr. Cohen's letter not to persist.

★   ★   ★

"I'm afraid I'm going to have to tell your parents," said Doctor Saul, carefully washing his hands after he had examined her. "Who is responsible for placing you in this position?"

Sylvia lowered her eyes; then she explained that she knew nothing whatsoever. It must have been obvious to the doctor that she was shielding someone.

"I'll write them a letter today," he continued. "They'll get it within the next few days."

"Oh, isn't there some way so that you don't have to

tell them?" asked Sylvia desperately.

"I'm sorry." He shook his head. "Normally what happens in my surgery between a doctor and a patient is confidential. But, because you are under age, it would be impossible for me not to notify them."

She left the surgery with her mind in turmoil. What on earth was she going to do? Perhaps her friend Veronica could help. It was ages since she had seen her, but she knew that Veronica's mother had said once that she would look after her. Deep in her heart, she knew that it wouldn't work. There was no way out. Instead of going back to school, she found herself walking in the direction of the fairground.

Danny spotted her immediately and came hurrying up.

"Hullo! What are you doing here? I thought you'd be at school."

"I just didn't feel like going today," she replied honestly.

"Why don't you come and meet my mum? She can tell your fortune."

At this moment, Sylvia wasn't at all sure that wanted her fortune told, nevertheless, she followed him into a cream-painted caravan.

Meeting Rosa, Sylvia could see where Danny had got his looks. She was swarthy like her son, with dark hair partially hidden under a bright scarf. A few tendrils poked out wispily at the sides of her ears which were adorned with large gold hoop ear-rings.

"Sit down, my dear," she said kindly, "and let me look at your hands. My, you have a lucky face."

Sylvia was feeling far from lucky, but she didn't say so. Danny came into the room carrying a large bowl of mutton stew.

"Get the bowls out, Danny," said Rosa. "I'm sure our young guest won't say no to a nice bit of stew, will you?"

Sylvia had to confess that it did smell good, and suddenly she realised that she was very hungry. She ate with relish. When she had finished and wiped her plate clean with a piece of bread, she leant back in her chair and rubbed her stomach. She was aware of Rosa's quick eyes following her every move.

"Thank you very much for the meal," she said, smiling at the woman.

"You're most welcome." Rosa still watched her keenly. "Now, is there anything else you want to tell Rosa? Anything at all?"

Sylvia glanced at Danny, who was sitting opposite. Rosa was quick to grasp the point.

"Go outside and help the rest of the men, Danny," she said.

The boy rose reluctantly. He had wanted to stay and listen.

"Now then," said Rosa encouragingly when they were alone. "Do you want to talk?"

Without quite knowing why, Sylvia felt that she could trust this woman. Hesitantly at first, she found herself telling her about the baby, though she made sure to omit any mention of her relationship with her father.

Rosa nodded understandingly, noting the girl's pale

face and tightly clenched hands which were lying in her lap.

"Would you like me to help you?" she asked gently, when she had finished.

"Could you?" stammered Sylvia.

"Well, I can try. Us Romanies have ways and means. Of course you will have to stay for a time with us."

"I can't!" wailed Sylvia. "Everyone will wonder where I am."

"Listen to me. You'll be perfectly safe and you can go home once it's all over. Just trust me."

Sylvia had no alternative. Either she could stay here until it was all over, whatever that meant, or she would have to go home and face her parents – who would know that she was going to have a baby and who would be waiting to punish her yet again.

Slowly she nodded her head.

"Good," said Rosa, satisfied. "Now, I'm going to tell Danny that you're our guest for a little while. Don't worry. There's no need for him to know anything else," she added, noticing Sylvia's expression. "Just you stay and relax. Don't fret about a thing. You're safe now with Rosa."

When Danny came back, he took Sylvia out to meet some of the other members of the fair.

"I hear you're going to stay with us for a while," he said. "Is that right?"

" 'Fraid so," she replied. To her relief, he did not question her further.

Danny had lived alone with his mother for several

years now, ever since the day of the accident. His father, along with others, had been erecting the caterpillar, when a big metal pole had suddenly come loose and crashed down, pinning him under it. By the time the men had managed to pull him out, he was dead. It was a sad day for all of them, as he had been their leader for a number of years. He was a true Romany, being the seventh son of a seventh son. Danny had vowed then that one day he would follow in the family tradition and become leader.

The fair was due to open the next day. Rosa decided that nothing would be done until Sylvia had been round and seen everything, and all without having to pay a penny piece. The girl was so excited. She loved the noise. The smell of frying onions and candy floss were all a new experience for her. When it got dark, she ventured out of the caravan, holding onto Danny, who had strict instructions to look after her. Rosa sat in a tent with a big poster outside proclaiming that she was Madame Rosa, and could see into the future if you crossed her palm with silver.

All Sylvia's favourite records were being played as the rides went round and round. She went in the Ghost Train with Danny, who quite unexpectedly stole a kiss when she screamed and clutched him tight. He took her on the Big Wheel and the Dodgems. He won her a teddy bear on the Hoop La. She thought she had never enjoyed herself so much.

Chapter Eight

The policeman chewed on the end of his pencil.

"I must say this is an unusual case," he said after a time. "You say there's been no trouble at home? And she's never run off before?"

"Well, no! She had to go to the doctor's yesterday morning. Apart from that we've no idea what's made her do this," replied Mrs. Short, twisting her hands together distractedly.

The policeman noticed that the father kept out of the questioning and was looking decidedly nervous.

"Can you throw any light on the situation, sir?" he said, turning to him.

"I don't think so officer. My wife has told you all we know."

"All right. Well, don't worry! I don't expect she's far away. Sometimes kids need a while to sort themselves out. Anyway, I'll put an announcement in the local press and notify my superiors. We'll get a few posters run off from this picture. Would you say she looks like this now – at the present moment?"

"Yes, it's a good likeness," said Mrs. Short. "Only, of course, she was wearing her school clothes at the time of her disappearance."

"Are you sure she hasn't taken a spare set of clothes with her?"

"No, I've checked her bedroom. She has some savings in a bottle and that hasn't been touched."

"Very well, then. If we have any news, I'll contact you immediately."

"Thank you very much for your time," said Mrs. Short, showing the officer out.

★   ★   ★

At about this time, Sylvia was safely tucked up in bed at the caravan at the Park.

Rosa was bustling around. A large saucepan was boiling away on the cooker and the air was filled with the sweet smell of herbs and spices.

"What are you doing, Rosa?" she asked, raising her head.

The woman moved across to her and gently placed a hand on Sylvia's brow. Smoothing the hair away from her face, she crooned:

"You're going to be all right. Soon you will have a

nice warm drink which will make you sleep. Then, when you wake, it will be all over."

Sylvia believed her: Rosa was so kind and she trusted her. Nevertheless, she had to admit that she felt scared, and said as much.

"It's nothing, child," Rosa assured her. "I've helped lots of people in your situation, even though they were not so young."

She then went on to explain the healing properties of the various herbs and how they were used for curing all sorts of illnesses.

Sylvia took the cup that was handed to her. She lifted it to her lips. It smelt nice. She drank a little and found it not unpleasant. Soon she began to feel light-headed and her eyes became heavy. Rosa grasped her hands in her own and began singing to her in a strange tongue. Desperately now, Sylvia began to fight against the drowsiness, but it was more than she could do. The moment of panic subsided and she slipped into a dreamless sleep . . . .

Rosa turned to Old Meg who had been on hand throughout.

Meg was one of the original old gypsies with a face tanned like leather and several teeth missing, which gave her a crone – like look.

"Well," she said, filling her pipe and looking down at the sleeping child, "at least it's all over for her now. By the way, did you know we had the rozzers nosing around? They were looking for her. I told them we don't like strangers poking their noses in and they cleared off," she chuckled.

"She'll be safe here for a few more days," declared Rosa, clearing up the bloodstained towels. "Then we'll have to let her go."

* * *

Sylvia's eyes gradually focused on the inside of the caravan. She tried to lift her head from the pillows, but the pain was too intense. She felt a deep aching her belly and she cried aloud.

Rosa came bustling over.

"Ah, good! At last the princess awakes. Here, drink this." She held out a mug of sweet warm tea. "You'll soon feel better and be up and about again."

Sylvia took the mug and sipped the liquid. She felt better almost immediately.

"When can I go home?" she asked.

"In a day or so," Rosa replied. "I want to see that you're completely recovered first."

"Is everything all right now? You know, about the baby, I mean."

"It's all been taken care of. Nothing for you to worry about. There will be no baby now. Rosa has done her job. Sleep now . . ."

* * *

Sylvia bade them farewell with tears in her eyes. Rosa was not to know, but she had dreaded going home. She was grateful for all they had done and only wished that she could have stayed with Rosa and Danny.

They had shown her so much kindness. She felt secure with them; never again would she hear a word said against the gypsies.

"Don't forget what I told you to tell them at home," said Rosa, smiling and stroking her hair. "Remember, it's our secret." How could she guess at the depth of the girl's secret anguish?

"I won't, and thank you once again."

Rosa disappeared inside the caravan, leaving Danny and Sylvia alone.

"I'll never forget you," said Sylvia shyly, looking down at her feet.

Danny took her face between his hands and gently turned it towards his.

"I want you to take this," he said, handing her a chain with half an old medallion on it. While Sylvia was recovering from her ordeal, he had asked his mother if he could take it and cut it in half so that he could give one half to Sylvia. "It was my father's," he added by way of explanation. "I have the other half on a chain round my neck. Wear it always and think of me. I will never be far away."

Sylvia could hardly see through the tears that streamed down her face. She had a lump in her throat which almost choked her.

"It's all right, I understand. You don't have to say anything. Just think of me sometimes." He held her face in his hands and kissed her very gently on her mouth. "Maybe one day when you're all grown up, you'll come back and see Danny. And then, who knows . . .?"

★ ★ ★

"Where have you been?" cried June, running up behind her friend. "Your mum's going to kill you! I've been so worried about you! So have Mum and Dad."

"I had to go away. Right away."

"But where?"

"It's a secret. I can't tell you."

"Go on. You can tell me. I promise I won't breathe a word to a living soul. Anyway, I am your friend."

"I can't tell you or anyone," replied Sylvia.

June looked offended. "All right," she said. "Please yourself."

"Sorry. I don't mean to be rude, but really I can't . . . Maybe one day," Sylvia said helplessly.

June linked her arm through Sylvia's and accompanied her as far as the front gate.

"Don't forget," she said. "I'm only next door if you need me."

Sylvia rang the door bell. It was opened almost immediately by her mother who had seen her coming down the road.

"Sylvia! What do you think you've been playing at? I've had half the police force in London round here looking for you! Oh, the shame of it all! I can hardly face the neighbours. What must they be thinking? Well! Are you just going to stand there looking like an imbecile?"

"I'm sorry," said Sylvia simply, shrugging her shoulders.

"Sorry! Sorry? Is that all you can say? Your father

and I have been at our wits' end. You'd best get upstairs and take off those dirty clothes. When you've finished you can come downstairs, I have a letter to show you that needs an explanation."

Oh God she knows, thought Sylvia, her heart almost dropping in her shoes. How on earth do I get out of this one? Do I tell her the truth? Do I lie to protect him, what shall I do?

Wiping a cold wet flannel over her face and behind her ears, Sylvia studied herself in the cracked mirror above the washbasin. She looked fairly normal, not at all as if she had been to hell and back. Her face was rather pale, but she noticed the dark shadows under her eyes. Apart from feeling very tired, she didn't feel any different. Only her body knew the truth, and now, so did her mother it seemed.

★   ★   ★

"What's the meaning of this?" her mother demanded, thrusting the official looking envelope under Sylvia's nose. "This is a letter from Doctor Saul." Each word was emphasised slowly. "In it he says you're pregnant, is this true?"

Sylvia, in her fright started to stammer.

"Of course it's true," her mother continued. "Why would he want to write me a pack of lies? You little slut! You filthy little slut! How dare you bring shame on our family. We are decent people, well respected people and now, this disgrace, after all we have done for you!"

86

Sylvia managed to find her voice. "I'm sorry. Yes it is true, although . . . only . . . I'm not now you see . . . That's why I ran away . . ." her voice trailed off at the look in her mother's eyes.

Mrs Short made towards her daughter who was by now cowering in the corner of the room. Raising her hand and bringing it down heavily, she aimed a massive blow to the side of Sylvia's head. Sylvia tried to shield her head from this vicious attack, but to no avail. Mrs Short then grabbed her daughter by the hair, pulled her to her feet and began punching and kicking at her body with all the force she could muster, arms flailing wildly. There was no reasoning with her. She was completely out of control. Her actions spoke of a woman demented.

Keeping up the attack on her daughter, which must have lasted two minutes, but to Sylvia, seemed like two hours, she finally pushed her daughter away. She was white with fury and now stood panting heavily, trying to catch her breath. She felt exhausted but triumphant when she looked at Sylvia. She noted with glee the bruises that were evident around the child's face. She laughed wildly at the bloodied nose. Yes! She had done a good job. No one will look at her now with her face all puffy and swollen. No one will want to touch her looking like that! She couldn't see the real harm that she had inflicted on her daughter. She didn't even think of the outcome of her onslaught on the child. All she could see was her own satisfaction at bringing her daughter down a peg or two.

Finally, worn out by this ruthless attack, Mrs Short

sat down and laughed. Anyone seeing her would have thought her truly mad. She kept laughing hysterically before telling Sylvia to "Get up and get out of my sight, you worthless trollop."

Sylvia picked herself painfully up from the floor where she had finally fallen. Limping heavily, she leaned on the banisters for support as she dragged her aching body up to the bedroom. As she undressed for bed, she caught sight of her face in the wardrobe mirror. She was horrified at what she saw. Her left eye was split and oozing blood. The right eye was almost closed. Her nose was bleeding too. In fact, her face looked a complete mess. She hardly dared to look at the rest of her body, although curiosity overcame her. She took off all her clothes and stood before the long mirror. Her arms and almost all her body was covered in bruises that were slowly turning purple. Hardly any part of her body had escaped the attack by her mother. Wincing with pain, Sylvia crawled into bed and pulled the cover tightly over her head as if to ward off any further abuse. The sheets felt cold against her body which was by now burning with pain. Oh how she hoped her father wouldn't demand to see her and punish her even further. She didn't think her body could take any more. Like her heart, it felt broken. What had she really done to make this spiteful woman despise her so? She had tried so hard to make her mother love her, to be proud of her. And the funniest thing of all she thought, was that her mother had'nt even asked who was the baby's father. She then too laughed hysterically, before collapsing into streams of tears that seemed as if they would never stop.

* * *

It was over a week since Sylvia had returned home. As was usual these days, the atmosphere round the table for the evening meal was strained. Sylvia seemed unhappy and withdrawn in her father's company, and Mr. Short himself had relapsed into a moody silence from which his wife found it impossible to draw him.

When Sylvia left the table, the cloud failed to lift. This evening, Mrs. Short decided that she could take no more of it. It had gone on long enough.

Her husband became aware of her looking at him, and leaned back in his chair. "What's wrong?" he asked testily.

"I was just thinking how quiet this house is," she remarked.

He sighed irritably, and began rolling a cigarette between his slim fingers. "I really don't know what you have to complain about. You have Sylvia back now and everything's fine. She's promised not to do anything like that again. What more do you want?"

Mrs. Short pursed her lips angrily.

"Now you just listen to me for a minute," she began in a cool voice. "Things here have changed. Oh, they weren't that great before. But they're even worse now. Your drinking has started up again, and you never talk to the girl. I feel sure you're both hiding something from me and I want to know what it is. You're as bad as each other; there's nothing to choose between you! Did she tell you why she ran away? I know she's always preferred you to me – well, at least up to now. I can't say that I blame her. I don't love her, and that's that. She has always been an outsider to me."

Mr. Short appeared to be listening, although he wasn't really interested in his wife's opinion. He sat there, intense and quiet, while she berated him, his dark, moody eyes never leaving her face. As soon as she stopped for breath, he leaned forward over the table.

"Now let me speak!" he said in a low, husky voice. "You say that I'm inconsiderate where Sylvia's concerned. Well, I'll tell you this – I love that child. It's there inside me." He tapped his chest as he spoke. "I've tried to give her a little comfort, a little compassion and a little love. Yes, love! Something you've never shown to her or me. Call yourself a mother? I'm only too thankful that we never had children of our own. John is your blue-eyed boy, and don't we all know it? It makes me sick how you go on about him all the time. What about Sylvia? Oh no, of course she doesn't count! I'm not surprised she ran away from home. And if she does it again, you've only yourself to blame. You were never concerned about her. All you cared about was what the neighbours would think. Never mind about Sylvia!"

Mrs. Short stared at him open-mouthed, trying to fathom out what he was really saying.

"Are you – in love with her?" she asked slowly.

"Love?" echoed her husband, his face flushing as

he clenched his fists on the table. He paused for a moment, then he stared hard at her and grimaced. "All right! You won't be satisfied until you know the truth, so I'm going to tell you. Perhaps then you'll understand."

The light from the glowing coals flickered on the high ceiling as he began to speak. He told of his dismay when Mrs. Short had first found that she could not have any children; of her subsequent coldness towards him; of how, more recently, he had had his suspicions about Mr. Cohen. She sat silent throughout and, when finally he sank back in his chair, she stood up and left the room without saying a word.

What she didn't know was that her husband hadn't told her the whole truth. She was still unaware that he had interfered with Sylvia. He had spoken mostly about herself and she didn't like what she heard. The only good thing to come of it all was that, from that day on, Mr. Short left his daughter alone.

Chapter Nine

It was the thirty-first of December, 1958, the threshold of a new year. Christmas in the Short household had been far from happy. Mrs. Short was a changed woman since the talk with her husband several months earlier. He had made it plain that he knew about her affair with Mr. Cohen. How he had found out was a mystery to her: she thought she had been so careful. His plain speaking had done nothing to endear him to her. His drinking was getting worse; he was drunk nearly every day now. She could hardly bear him near her. If, in the night, he accidentally turned over and touched her with his foot, she would give an involuntary shudder and push him away. Recently she had begun placing a pillow the length of the bed between them so that she would have no contact with him at all. If they had the room, they would certainly have been occupying separate bedrooms.

Also, although she kept this from the rest of the household Mrs. Short was not a well woman. Doctor Saul had told her that she ought to go into hospital for an operation on her womb. She had various cysts which needed to be removed. It was because of these that she had failed to have any children. She didn't want to go – in fact, she actually resisted it – because for once in her life she was afraid of the consequences. She was in a great deal of pain, nevertheless, she preferred to carry on as she was.

The clock struck midnight and the sound of revellers welcoming the new year carried on the night air. Mrs. Short put down her knitting and stole a glance at her husband. He was asleep, snoring like a pig, his mouth slackly gaping. How disgusting he was! She despised him. Was this the handsome man who had captured her heart all those years ago? This drooling, dribbling mess of a man?

It was all because of Sylvia, she thought, that things had not worked out as she had hoped. Why on earth couldn't they have just adopted the boy?

Thinking of Sylvia always made her angry now. The girl was in her final year at school, and had shown signs of being very bright. The headmistress had absurd ambitions for her, as she had learnt when they met just before the school broke up in December. All that nonsense about Sylvia going to College! Ridiculous! Girls went out to work and then got married and had babies. Anyway, John had left school at fifteen and was now working as an apprentice in an electrical shop in Maxted Road. Sylvia could work in a shop, too, she decided.

She wound up her knitting, banked down the fire and climbed the stairs to bed, leaving her husband snoring in his chair.

* * *

During her final months at school, Sylvia's work gradually deteriorated. She felt it useless to try to achieve good marks. Her headmistress was dismayed by the change that had come over her and one day, cornering her in the school library, she asked her why she was not trying this term. Sylvia explained that she felt there was no point as her mother wouldn't let her go on to college. She had hoped to do a journalism course and eventually work for a large newspaper company. But her dreams of this had been shattered when Mrs. Short had told her:

"I have looked after you, clothed you and fed you for the past fourteen years. Now it's your turn to pay me by going to work. I don't want to hear any more nonsense about staying on for further education. You'll get married eventually, so there's no point in carving out a career for yourself. I need your money, and you *DO* owe me!"

Only one of Sylvia's friends was staying on at school to do a typing course, and that was June. How Sylvia envied her!

94

They were at Fred's Cafe and the melodious strains of The Platters singing 'Smoke Gets in Your Eyes' could be heard above the chatter. Sylvia liked the song. Its haunting melody brought her close to tears. Why had they ever adopted her? She had never felt wanted. Her life was all wrong. She wished she had parents like other children. Mr. Short didn't come near her now and she was grateful for that. But, at the same time, he never showed her the love he claimed once to have felt for her. Sometimes she secretly wished that he would come to her bedroom, just to say that he loved and cared for her. All she had was her school and her friends. Very soon she wouldn't even have that. Her books were still her escape, although now her reading habits had changed. Last week she had read 'Little Woman' and had cried over the sad bits. Now she had started on 'Jane Eyre' and was enjoying that, too.

"Sorry, June. What did you say?"

"Gosh, you were miles away! I said: 'Why don't we go to One Tree Hill on Sunday if it's nice?'"

Sylvia liked One Tree Hill. It was a place where she normally went on her own just to think and laze. She took her books with her and would read until dusk, then return home late and be bombarded with questions about where she had been. The Shorts were always convinced that she was up to no good. They had no trust in her these days. She didn't blame them. It was her fault for running away from home last year.

She smiled at June. "Yes, I'd like that."

"Good! That's settled then; I'll get mum to pack us a picnic."

The previous week, the two girls had made a pact. They each pricked one of their fingers with a pin and, mingling their blood, had proclaimed that they were blood sisters. They buried a matchbox filled with little letters in Sylvia's front garden. Years later, they would dig it up to see what they had written on that day.

When Sylvia reached home, she rushed upstairs to the bedroom and looked at herself in the mirror. She had been told at school that her eyes were like Elvis Presley's. Yes, she could definitely see a likeness! Wouldn't it be wonderful if she was related to him! She could go and live in America and have all the money she wanted. She made a mental note to write to him and ask him if he had a long lost sister?

* * *

Sunday was warm and sunny. Sylvia pecked her mother on the cheek and went next door to call on her friend.

"Come in, lovey," said June's mother. "She won't be long. I've made a lovely picnic for you both. You do like ginger beer, don't you?"

"Oh yes, Mrs. Johnson! Thanks ever so much."

Mrs. Johnson leant over the banisters. "How much longer are you going to be June? Whatever are you doing up there? Sylvia's waiting for you."

"Be right down, Mum."

June came slipping downstairs while her mother was in the kitchen. She was holding a carrier bag behind her back.

"Quick!" she hissed at Sylvia. "Let's get going."

"What have you got in that bag?"

"Can't tell you now. Come on! Bye, Mum!" she shouted.

"Don't you two get up to any mischief now!" came the reply.

The door banged behind them and they were on their way.

They were at the top of the road and out of sight of the house when June opened the bag. In it were two pairs of her mother's shoes, a tube of smarties and an eyebrow pencil.

"What are you going to do with them?" asked Sylvia, a puzzled frown creasing her brow.

"I'll show you," smiled June. She led her friend by the hand to the toilets in the swing park and got to work. Presently she said: "You look everso pretty, Sylvia. You've got a lovely smile. Here, look at your-self." She handed her a tiny mirror.

"Teeth too big," Sylvia muttered, and then wished she hadn't. Her family and friends were always making uncomplimentary remarks about this feature, calling them tombstones or rabbit teeth.

Peering into the mirror, she gave a gasp of surprise. Why, it was true, she did look almost pretty! Her hair was shaped in the style of the Kaye Sisters – short, straight and sleek and cut in a fringe. Her mouth had been painted with a red smartie and it was very con-vincing. She couldn't see the rest of her body, but she had on a pair of high heels, and June had drawn a line up her legs with an eyebrow pencil so that it looked as if she had stockings on.

"My turn now," declared June.

She waited patiently, while Sylvia did the same to her. Then, giggling, they stuffed their socks down the front of their frocks, padding them out nicely.

"There!" said June, twisting her head as she regarded herself in the mirror. "I think we'll do."

They tottered off unsteadily on their high heels, provoking wolf whistles from a couple of ten year old boys.

* * *

"Cor! Look at them two!" A boy with long side-burns, and dressed in a drape jacket and crepe-soled shoes, turned to his friend. "You can have the blonde one, Colin, and I'll have the dark-haired little cracker."

Colin, miffed, declared that he liked the dark-haired one too. Why should Peter have her? A mock fight broke out. Peter won and had first choice.

"Watch this!"

He went jauntily over to the two girls, who were waiting at the bus stop.

"Wotcher, darlings! Where's two gorgeous girls like you off to on this luverly afternoon?"

June nudged her friend. "See, I told you it'd work," she whispered. "What's it to do you with you?" she replied, cheekily.

"Well, it's like this, see. Me and my mate Colin

wanted to know if you'd like to go to Battersea Park with us?"

"Oh, I don't know about that," June said hesitantly. "We don't even know you."

"What's to know? I'm Peter and this one here's me mate Colin. There, we all know each other now. So how's about it then?"

"We'll think about it."

"Please yourself, but don't take too long over it. We're busy blokes," Peter said as nonchalantly as he knew how.

"They're Teds," whispered June. "What do you think?"

"I don't know. What do you think?" replied Sylvia, who had secretly made up her mind that it was a good idea and much better than spending the afternoon on their own.

"All right then, we'll come with you if you like," decided June, self-appointed spokeswoman.

"Luverly, darling! 'Ere, you put your arm through mine, Sylvia, and your mate can team up with Colin."

The two girls thought this was fun. They had heard a lot about Teddy Boys, and not all of it was good. Still, these two looked harmless enough, and they were smartly dressed!

They boarded a number two bus which set them down right outside the gates.

"Won't be a mo'," said June. "Just going to powder our noses."

Peter pulled a face. "Well, hurry it up. We've got a lot to do."

"All right! Don't worry."

As soon as they were on their own, June fished around in her bag and passed her friend a tissue. "Here, Sylvia, wipe your teeth! Your lipstick's gone all over the place."

"I wish it was real lipstick!" Sylvia moaned. "God, I look dreadful!"

"No, you don't! Those shoes of my mum's don't half suit you. Come on, let's not keep them waiting!"

On the bus coming home, Peter carelessly draped an arm around Sylvia's shoulders, letting his fingers play with the buttons on the back of her frock.

"Just what do you think you're doing?" she said, giving him a hefty smack.

"Nuffink, darling. Honest!" he protested, holding his hands aloft.

"I'm not your 'darling', so please stop calling me that."

"I'm not your darling eiver!" mimicked Peter. "Sorry," he added shamefacedly, seeing how upset she was. "Listen! You're a real doll and I like you. I only wanted to hold you. I didn't mean to make you upset."

"All right then," Sylvia looked into his eyes, which were dark brown; for a fleeting moment she was reminded of Danny.

"How about coming to the flicks next week?"

"If June wants to," his friend replied, turning to her for confirmation.

June nodded her head.

"I take it that means Yes, does it?"

June looked down and smiled coyly.

"Yes, mate. We're coming, too."

"Well?" Peter looked at Sylvia.

"I'd love to go with you," she added, smiling shyly.

A week sped by, and the next Saturday found the girls at the bus stop waiting for their boyfriends. Sylvia gazed at June in admiration.

"Where on earth did you buy it?" she asked.

"I didn't. I made it myself," June stated proudly, twirling around in her A-line pale lilac frock. It had a dropped waistline, a full skirt and lots of petticoats underneath.

"It's really beautiful! You're so clever, June!"

"I could teach you, if you want."

Sylvia pulled a face. She doubted if anyone could teach her needlework. She was absolutely hopeless. At school she had started on an apron when she was in the first year, and now that she was in the fourth year she was still nowhere nearer to finishing it.

"It's kind of you to offer," she sighed ruefully, "but I don't think I'll ever get the hang of making clothes."

"Never mind." June smiled at her encouragingly. "I'll never be as good as you at English. We can't all be good at the same things. Look! Here they come now!"

"Very nice, darling! Oh, that is nice!" said Colin as they approached.

"Right, off we go then." Peter took Sylvia's hand in his.

Sylvia felt herself go all warm inside. Peter made her feel protected and loved. She stole a sideways glance at him as they went along. He was looking very dapper today in his suit. It was brown with shiny lapels. His hair was gleaming in the sun where he had put a liberal blob of Brylcreme on it. It curled into the nape of his neck. He had a sprinkling of freckles across his nose, which in some undefined way, endeared her to him. She caught sight of some other girls gazing at him with envy and felt proud to be seen on his arm.

"I wish I had nice clothes to wear," she said.

"It's you I go out with, not your clothes," he replied.

Still, perhaps when she left school she would be able to buy all the clothes she liked. She was fed up with wearing hand-me-downs and frocks that were made too long. She was sick of hearing the same old story: "Plenty of room to grow."

June had done a good job with the make-up. She had managed to get hold of some real lipstick, mascara and eyeshadow this week. Her mother would have a fit if she could see her now, she thought.

They were rounding the corner by Goose Green when, to her dismay, she heard a voice calling her name.

"Sylvia! Sylvia! Is that really you?"

"Oh, crikey! It's my mum!" She began to tremble at once. It was far too late to even think of escape. Mrs. Short placed herself squarely in front of the four of them.

"What have we here then?" she demanded, eyeing them.

June began: "I can explain, Mrs. Short."

"I'm sure you can." Sylvia's mother looked her up and down, and her foot began to tap on the pavement.

"Come on then," she said, "explain yourself. I'm waiting."

"Well, you see, it's like this, Mrs. Short . . ." June faltered, by now quite unnerved. She had never liked Sylvia's mother and she could see that at present she was in an unforgiving mood.

Peter stepped into the breach. "Mrs. Short? It is Mrs. Short, isn't it?"

"Don't give me any of your glib tongue, boy! I want to know what you're doing walking down the street with your arm around my daughter."

"I happen to like your daughter."

"Oh! You do, do you? Well, let me tell you this. She's not fifteen yet and, what's more, I don't allow her to go out with boys. Any boys!" she added angrily, staring at Peter and noting his suit with disgust. "I know all about your sort. Going around, slashing seats! Flick knives and motor bikes!"

Then, as he stood there dumbstruck, she grabbed Sylvia by the arm and dragged her off down the road, the girl protesting weakly.

"What's up with her? The old dragon? Does she always behave like that?" Peter turned to June for some form of explanation.

June looked miserable as she watched her friend being dragged away by her mother. "I don't think she has a happy life at home. Mum and Dad feel sorry for her. Her parents are always arguing. I can hear them shouting at each other when I go to bed. The other week she had bruises all over her body. When my mum asked her how it happened, she went quiet and mumbled something about having fallen down the cellar stairs. I'm sure it was her father. Mum says we shouldn't get involved; that it's none of our business.

"Well, I still like Sylvia." declared Peter. "And when I'm older, I shall go up to her house, knock on the door and give her dad what for. Then grab Sylvia and run away to Gretna Green where we'll get married. Then no-one will ever find us!"

Colin and June laughed at this piece of information. How they would love to see Peter tackle Sylvia's parents!

"I'm glad my parents aren't like that." said June, sitting on a bench at Goose Green. "Guess I'm lucky really. I know they spoil me because I am their only child, but . . . sometimes I wish Sylvia was my sister. My mum gets really fed up with Mrs Short calling on her all the time. She pretends to be something she's not."

"What do you mean by that?" asked Colin.

Peter sat moodily picking at imaginary threads of fluff on his new brown trousers.

"Well. Oh you know. She thinks she's better than anyone else. She tries to speak posh. Do you know she actually pokes her little finger out when she's drinking a cup of coffee? Like this." June stuck her little finger out at an angle.

The three of them laughed at this exaggerated gesture.

"Why doesn't your Mum just tell her to get lost?" This came from Peter.

"She doesn't like to make bad friends, especially

with neighbours. Any way she's far too polite to say what she really means. My mum doesn't like offending people, so she puts up with it for the sake of peace and quiet. I know Dad would say something as he can't stand the family. Say's he doesn't trust them. I think he suspects that something awful is going on, but doesn't want to cause a fuss.

"Yes, I can understand that. But if something nasty is going on, shouldn't someone do something about it?" Peter cried, jumping to his feet. "I'm going to go round there right now and sort it out."

"Hold on a minute," said Colin, grabbing the sleeve of Peter's jacket. "You can't do anything on your own. Look, I'll come with you," he offered.

"No!" said Peter emphatically. "She's my girlfriend and I'll deal with it in my own way."

"What are you going to do?" asked June.

"Punch her dad on his nose. That's what I'm going to do!"

"But we've go no proof that he did beat her up, have we?" said June. " What I mean is that if Sylvia says that she fell down the cellar steps, who are we to disbelieve her. We might make matters worse." she added wisely.

"Suppose you're right." Peter admitted grudgingly.

"Well are we going to the flicks now? Colin asked brightly.

"I'm not in the mood." said June.

"Nor me." said Peter gloomily.

They sat on the bench and talked a while longer. After a time, they got up and made their separate ways home. Sylvia was in the thoughts of all of them. The afternoon that had started out so fine, sunny and full of promise, had ended on a sour note. Perhaps it was merciful that none of them knew just how unhappy the life was that Sylvia led at home.

*   *   *

It just wasn't fair! Sylvia sobbed into her pillow that night. She had really liked Peter. Now she doubted if she would ever see him again. Why did her mother have to show her up all the time? Why was she always taking her away from anything she had ever loved or wanted? Sniffing and drying her eyes, she thought she would be glad when she left school. When she had saved up enough money, she would leave this horrid house and never come back.

Chapter Ten

Sylvia looked gloomily out of the window through the thick frost which had formed on it overnight. This December day in 1959 was as dull and dreary as she felt herself. She had no reason to feel any joy. It was her last day at school and she was miserable. Still, it could have been worse. Her fifteenth birthday hadn't been until October, or she would have been expected to leave school at the end of the summer term.

She forced herself to hurry and pulled on her clothes. All her instincts told her to take her time: she wished she could make this day last forever.

She walked to school alone as she had done ever since June had left in July. June was now attending secretarial course in Wandsworth and was doing very well. As she trailed along, Sylvia looked across at windswept park with its trees bereft of leaves, and thought of Danny and Rosa. She wondered where they were now and how they were. Her half of the medallion was on the chain she wore around her neck. Danny had insisted that she wear it always, and she had tried her best to, but it hadn't been easy keeping it from her mother's eagle eyes.

Suddenly she was aware of running footsteps behind her, and Gloria overtook her.

"Hang on a minute!" she cried. "Are you deaf or what?"

"What?" asked Sylvia, distractedly.

"I've been calling you for at least a minute."

"Sorry," replied Sylvia. "I was deep in thought."

"Yes, it looked like it. Actually, I wanted to ask if you'd like to come to Fred's cafe. I've got a couple of bob and as it's the last day of school, they can hardly tell us off for being late, can they?"

Sylvia hesitated. "I don't think we ought to," she began. Then she shrugged. "Oh well! What difference can it make? Let's go!"

Fred greeted them kindly, and asked if they had come to play the juke box again.

"Of course," said Gloria. "But we also want two cups of your best coffee."

"No, Gloria. I don't think we've got time for that," said Sylvia pulling at her friend's sleeve.

"Well, I've got time," replied Gloria stubbornly, "and so have you. Listen, it's our last day! Who cares?" Sylvia did not argue with her, and Gloria added: "What record do you want then? Something Christmassy or what?"

"I don't mind. It's your money."

They decided on 'Oh Carol', 'What Do You Want', 'Jingle Bell Rock' and 'Sea of Love'. Marty Wilde was just finishing 'Sea of Love' when Sylvia looked at the clock above the counter.

"My God!" she gasped. "We're going to be half an hour late. Let's run."

* * *

Miss Simpson had taken off her spectacles and was wiping her eyes.

"I think she's going to cry," whispered Gloria to Sylvia. It was incredible but true: their stalwart unflappable teacher seemed to be on the verge of tears.

"I shall miss you all," she said, drawing a deep breath. "I have known you girls since the first form. I hope you all have a good future in whatever you do. This will be my last year at Friern, too. Next summer I am retiring, and I shall go back to my home near the Dordogne. I still have some relatives living there, and . . ."

"Please, Miss," Sylvia interrupted her, putting up her hand, "where is Dordogne?"

"Well, Sylvia. It's a river in South West France, which flows to join the Garonne and form the Gironde estuary." Miss Simpson's eyes took on a distant look as she spoke of her beloved country.

Sylvia vaguely remembered learning about it in a

geography lesson. Then Miss Simpson startled her by clapping her hands together. Declaring that this would never do, she quickly turned round to write some information on the blackboard.

"We'll tidy up today," she told them. "There's no point in my setting any exercises. And I'd like you all to tell me about what you intend to do with your life outside school."

One by one, the girls stood up and said their piece. When Sylvia's turn came, she confessed that she didn't really care what happened to her. Coming from a girl who had shown so much promise in her school work, this was a disappointment for her teacher. The child appeared to have lost her way. Still, it was not Miss Simpson's worry. The session ended, and the last farewells were said.

What a sad day this was for Sylvia. As she gathered up her belongings, she stole a glance around the classroom that had been her home for the past four years. School had been her haven, her retreat; now she had nothing. Oh, no doubt Mother had a boring job lined up for her, but her heart wouldn't be in it. She belonged here, with all her friends, but they were going, too. What had fate got in store for her?

She took the long way home, walking through the park where the policeman had caught them smoking that time. She, with four others, had been having a puff: to make it last longer, they had put a hairgrip on the end of the cigarette. It came to her turn and she had just placed it in her mouth when the policeman came around the corner on his bicycle and caught them – or rather her.

"Drop that!" he said sternly. "If I catch you doing that again, I shall inform your parents."

She had dropped it and run like the wind, followed by her four friends. Once out of sight, they had dared her to go back and pick it up. When she reached the place, she found the policeman had put his foot on it and stamped it into the ground.

"Shame!" the others had chorused, when she returned to where they were standing and told them. Then, looking around to make sure the policeman had gone, they lit another one.

She smiled to herself. Those had been good times!

She was vexed to find that her mother was home early. She could have done with being on her own tonight.

"That's it then!" Mrs. Short's voice came to her from the scullery.

Suddenly the tears that had been threatening all day burst forth. It was like opening the floodgates.

Mrs. Short appeared out of the scullery, wiping her hands on her pinny.

"Whatever are you crying for?"

"I miss school!"

"Miss school? You must have something wrong with your brain. Everyone else is glad to see the back of it, but not you. Why do you always have to be different?"

Sylvia kept silent. How could she possibly explain? Her mother would never understand in a million years. Only she knew how she felt.

"Now we have to find you a job, and I know just the place. I'll take you there after Christmas," Mrs. Short continued. "The sooner you start earning some money to pay for what I've done for you, the better."

Early in the new year, they set off for Marks and Spencers in Rye Lane. Mrs. Short had insisted on accompanying Sylvia, and she looked smart, if over-dressed, in her new fur coat with a dead fox fur draped over her shoulders. Sylvia hated that fox with its dead eyes that stared blankly at her. She felt as if it could see her innermost feelings. Three other girls were also waiting to be interviewed; but, unlike her, they weren't dressed in white ankle socks and the black lace-up shoes that were called 'Beetle Crushers'. And they didn't have their mothers with them. It made Sylvia feel stupid and awkward, sitting there.

Needless to say, she didn't get a job. Afterwards, humiliated by her failure, she asked her mother why she felt it necessary to go with her for job interviews. All Mrs. Short would say was that she had gone with John to get his and she would do the same with her daughter. It seemed to Sylvia that she couldn't even have a mind of her own. Her life was being totally dominated.

Eventually, her mother found her a job at Jones and Higgins, which was a big family departmental store on the corner of Rye Lane and Peckham High Street. It made Sylvia sick to see her mother sucking up to the manager of the baby wear department, where later she discovered that she was to work. She was told that her wages would be three pounds and fifteen shillings a week. Mrs. Short had already made it quite clear that she was to bring her pay packet home unopened and that she would require the sum of three pounds and ten shillings towards Sylvia's upkeep. The five shillings that remained would be Sylvia's, to spend as she wished. Out of that five shillings, she had to find her bus fares, dinner money and clothes.

* * *

Mrs. Short excelled herself as she prepared her daughter for her first day at work. She had bought her some white blouses and two black skirts, along with a pair of stockings and some neat flat casual black shoes. What a change from the ugly black lace-ups!

"You have to create a good impression." was all she would say when Sylvia tried to thank her.

Sylvia was the youngest in the baby wear department; the other staff consisted of a middle-aged woman named Violet and a much older woman, Edna. They had been at the store since leaving school and knew everything there was to know about the stock. They were kind to the friendless girl and took her under their wing; with their help and guidance, Sylvia actually found herself liking the job.

She had been there for three months when she was called into the manager's office.

"Sit down," he said, clearing his throat. "Now then, how long have you been with us, Miss Short?"

"Three months, sir," Sylvia replied timidly.

"Well now! Your good work has led to your being here with me today. I'm very pleased with what you've picked up in the short time you've been with us, and I think you are due for a slight raise in salary."

Sylvia nearly pinched herself. She thrived on praise and could hardly believe her good fortune.

"So," he went on, "I think it only right that we show our appreciation by giving you another five shillings a week. How does that suit?"

Sylvia thought that it would suit very nicely. She could buy some extra clothes now that she would have ten shillings to herself.

"I'm very grateful. Thank you very much, sir," she replied, blushing.

"Very well. You may go," he said, waving his hand in dismissal. "Oh yes, one more small point! In a fortnight's time, Edna will be retiring. I wondered whether you would like to train to become our next baby wear buyer?"

"Me, sir?" Sylvia's face was bright red.

"Why not? You're a bright girl; you could have a good future with us. Now, I don't want to hear any more on the subject. You'll go on the course as soon as possible."

Sylvia left his office hugging herself with glee. She was sure her mother, too, would be pleased with this news!

Certainly Mrs. Short was pleased. "Another five shillings, you say? Yes, that'll be a useful contribution to the family income."

Sylvia was outraged. What about all the things she

could do with that extra money? What about her new clothes?

"What do you mean?" she wailed.

"I think you know only too well what I mean. It will help pay your way in this household, and that is then end of the subject," Mrs. Short said firmly, her mouth set in a grim line.

During her lunch break the next day, Sylvia went into Woolworth's and asked for a job there. She had to take a simple arithmetic test, which she passed easily. They told her that the starting wage for her age was four pounds and ten shillings. Making a quick mental calculation, she reckoned that, after paying her mother the three pounds fifteen shillings she required, she would still have fifteen shillings left. That would keep everyone happy, she decided.

Mrs. Short raged at her. "Are you mad?" she said. "Throwing away a good job like that!"

Sylvia hadn't told her how much Woolworth's were prepared to pay her and she hoped she had got away with it. Her hopes were dashed when Mrs. Short told her that she expected to see her wage packet unopened. She groaned inwardly. Was there nothing she could do that would not be foiled by her mother? She despaired of ever looking nice and wearing modern clothes like other girls.

Woolworth's was a complete disaster! What happened was this: she found herself working on the plant counter. Some of the plants looked really moth-eaten. She didn't see how anyone could have the cheek to charge one and sixpence for specimens like that.

When a customer came in who looked poor, she would only charge them one shilling. An elderly lady was so grateful that she went and told a supervisor about the kind young lady on the plants. Consequently, unknown to Sylvia, she was watched and finally called into the manager's office, where she was told that they were dispensing with her services. She had got the sack simply for helping others! She had thought herself a bit like Robin Hood, robbing the rich to help the poor. What on earth was she going to tell them at home.

★ ★ ★

"Lost your job? And where do you think you're going to get the money to pay for your board and keep?" Mrs. Short's face was purple with rage,

"I'm sorry. I'll look for something else tomorrow. There's a place at . . ."

Her mother stormed towards her, hands flailing wildly. Sylvia tried to protect her face as the blows rained down. She felt her hair being grabbed and pulled at the roots, then her head was banged against the wall. One of her hands was clawed by her mother's fingernails and blood was drawn. Suddenly Mrs. Short flung her from her in disgust.

"I don't know why I bother with you," she said. "You are bad through and through. One day you'll end up in prison because you're so bad. Go to your room now, your father will deal with you when he gets home."

Sylvia lay in bed, waiting. She heard the front door go and muffled voices conferring downstairs. Then footsteps sounded on the stairs. Suddenly her father was in her bedroom.

"What's all this about losing your job? We rely on your money, you know." He stood looking down at her: by now she was shaking all over. She turned her face to the wall, convinced that something bad was about to happen.

He was silent for a moment, as if regarding her thoughtfully, but he made no move to come near. After a while he spoke again, in a kinder tone.

"You must realise that we depend on your wage to live comfortably. You'll have to get another job, and quickly!"

"Yes, Dad," she said meekly. "I was going to tell Mother that there's an office job going at David Rose, the wholesale grocer's in the Old Kent Road. One of my friends that I went to school with told me about it."

"That's a bit of a way to travel to work. Wouldn't it be more sensible for you to work locally, where you won't have to pay bus fares?"

"I've already thought of that. The thing is, the wages are better than round here – and I could give Mother quite a bit extra," she said eagerly. "I know she'd be pleased about that."

"I'm not too sure she would be pleased with anything you do," said her father, rubbing the day old stubble on his chin. "All right. I'll talk to her and see what she says. You go to sleep now. Tomorrow's another day."

Then, giving her an absent-minded kiss on the cheek, he left her and went into the bathroom next door. After a few minutes she heard his feet heavily descending the stairs.

★   ★   ★

The interview at the grocer's was arranged for nine-thirty. Sylvia caught the bus to the Old Kent Road with a sick feeling in her stomach. She hated interviews! She never knew quite what to say. Luckily, she had managed to dissuade her mother from accompanying her on this occasion.

She arrived on the dot and waited in reception while the manager finished his phone call. After a bit, he poked his head round the door.

"Won't you please come in, Miss Short?" he said.

She found herself in an untidy office, stuffed floor to ceiling with books and papers.

"I apologise for this mess," he went on helplessly, waving an arm around the room. "I have just recently changed offices and haven't had time to clear things up yet." Sylvia was uncertain as to whether she was expected to make a comment; in the end she decided not to, and merely nodded.

During the course of the interview, the manager asked if she had any qualifications such as invoicing and typing. She explained that she had never worked in an office, but would be more than willing to learn. He appeared impressed by her frankness and decided to give her a month's trial. He explained what this meant and also that she would have to work a week in hand.

Even as he spoke, Sylvia thought how unfair this was. She was of the opinion that if you worked for a person for a whole week, then you should have money at the end of it. She understood that if she left the job, then she would have two weeks' wages instead of one. But what if she stayed there forever? What then? Still, she decided that she would like to give the job a try; she would just have to explain the situation to her mother and hope that she would understand. So they shook hands and she agreed to start the following Monday at nine o' clock sharp.

She alighted from the bus at the Heaton Arms and crossed over the road to walk through Rye Passage. Suddenly she heard her name being called. She swung round: it was Gloria.

"I thought you'd be at work today." she said, pleased to see her friend.

"I was, but I was sent home because of my tonsils. Look," Gloria said, opening her mouth wide.

"Goodness!" declared Sylvia. "Your throat has little white spots on it." She peered closely. "And your tonsils are red raw and swollen. It must be very painful to talk."

"Um," said Gloria, nodding in agreement. "The doctor's given me some tablets; he said I ought to take the rest of the week off. I'm bored already!"

"I can come and see you if you like," suggested Sylvia helpfully. "I don't start my new job till next week."

"I thought you were at Jones and Higgins?"

"Oh no! I left there ages ago. I worked in Woolworth's for a while, until I got the sack."

"You what? You got the sack from Woolworth's!" exclaimed Gloria, incredulously. "You must have done something really bad."

"It wasn't that bad." Sylvia shrugged nonchalantly. "What are you doing now?"

"Nothing really. Just helping my auntie in the shop."

Gloria's aunt ran a small bakery at the top of Rye Lane.

"Listen," said Sylvia. "I'll pop home and tell my mother about the job. Then I'll come back and give you all the news up to date, if you want."

"Hurry up then. I'll get some cakes and ginger pop and we can have a good old talk."

Sylvia let herself in by the front door. Her mother was not in the scullery, which surprised her. Going upstairs, she was alarmed to find her lying on the bed looking very unwell.

"What's the matter?" she asked anxiously, noting Mrs. Short's pale face and the beads of sweat across her brow and the top of her lip.

"Nothing for you to worry about," came the curt reply. "I came over giddy and felt like a little lie down. It's only my age, you know."

Sylvia didn't know. She had no experience of such matters. She wanted to help, but she ended up by fussing over her mother.

"Oh, do stop that! I'm all right, really I am." It was

as if Mrs. Short couldn't bear to be beholden to her. "How did you get on?"

"I got the job and I start next Monday!" Sylvia replied proudly. She was pleased with herself for having achieved this on her own initiative, without any favours or special pleading. She went on to say what her wages would be; then she added the bit about having to work a week in hand. Mrs. Short was visibly vexed by this piece of information.

"What good is that? Eh? I can't support you on nothing. Who do you think is going to pay your bus fares for a fortnight?"

Sylvia hadn't thought of that. Her thoughts flew to the large gin bottle which was used to prop open her bedroom door. She knew that she must have at least three pounds in it, but she was reluctant to break into it. She had to keep that for emergencies.

"Could you lend me the money? Then I'll pay you back a bit each week?"

"Oh well, I suppose so," grumbled her mother. "But you'll also have to pay me the back money you owe me." Her eyes lit up greedily as she began to reckon how much that would be. Suddenly she said: "Now I'm tired. All I need is a bit of peace and quiet, which I won't get while you're fussing about. Haven't you got anything to do to keep you amused?"

"Well, if you're sure you're all right, I'll go to the library." Sylvia didn't like lying to her mother, but she knew that she still didn't approve of Gloria and her family. Mrs. Short was asleep before Sylvia even had time to leave the room.

*   *   *

Gloria was waiting for her at the back of the bakery.

"You took your time. I thought you weren't coming."

"Yes, sorry about that. My mother wasn't very well."

She followed her friend through into a small, comfortably furnished living room, and they sat down side by side on a settee. Sylvia could smell the fresh bread baking and felt her mouth watering. Gloria brought in two glasses and a plate of fresh jam doughnuts. Sylvia tucked in avidly. Then, through sugared lips, she asked why Gloria wasn't eating.

"My throat's still too sore," her friend explained, reaching for a glass of ginger beer. She took a long swallow. "Nice!" she continued, gasping for breath as the bubbles went up her nose. She gave a big burp and giggled. "I beg your pardon! Right! Tell me all about Woolworth's."

Sylvia laughed and began to explain about the miserable plants and how she thought she would sell them more easily if they were reduced.

"You're so funny!" said Gloria, by now reduced to tears of laughter.

On a more serious note, Sylvia went on to talk about the new job and her mother's meanness about money. "I'll never have anything decent to wear if she keeps taking all my wages," she said. "I can't live on five bob a week. There must be a way of saving money . . ."

"I know what," Gloria said eagerly. "You can

borrow my bike. I hardly ever use it now and you know how to ride it."

"Well, I don't know," said Sylvia dubiously. "I've never ridden in traffic before."

"Come on!" said Gloria, sounding suddenly exasperated. "It makes sense. It's got to save you a few bob a week."

"All right, then, I'll give it a try."

"Atta girl! Look, I always keep it here." Gloria led the way outside. The gleaming bike was in an old shed at the back. It still looked new. Gloria handed Sylvia a padlock key. "Feel free to come and take it whenever you want. My aunt won't mind."

Sylvia was overwhelmed by her friend's generosity and tried to express her thanks.

"Think nothing of it," said Gloria. "I know you'd help me if you could."

Sylvia thought ruefully that she could hardly help herself, let alone anyone else. Hoping her friend would soon be better, she said goodbye.

Chapter Eleven

Sylvia's new job at David Rose's made quite a change from shop work; she enjoyed most of it, but some things were pretty boring and she hated filing. She had just recently grasped how to do invoices. She found that because she was the most junior, she was given all the menial tasks. She worked along with lots of other women. Only a couple of them were near her own age. She sighed as she filled the big heavy tea urn with water. She seemed to spend most of her time in the canteen making tea for the rest of the staff. It was difficult to imagine that she could settle down to doing this kind of work for the rest of her life. Lunch times were the best part, when she would go down to the warehouse to eat her sandwiches and play with the kittens.

A stray cat had walked in one day and, because the warehouse was teeming with mice, it had been decided that the cat could stay and earn its keep. It was called Smudge and everyone had thought it was a tom until, a couple of weeks back, it was discovered that it had four kittens in a cardboard box. The warehouse men were good and didn't tell the manager, as they felt he would get rid of the cat and her kittens if he knew. All the kittens had been found homes by members of the staff.

Sylvia's favourite was a tiny tortoiseshell kitten with 'mascara smudges' and two clown's teardrops under the wide eyes. It was the eyes which had first caught her attention. They were haunting eyes, a pale blue with a hint of green depths, like clear meadow stream water. She had named her Prudence and they were great friends.

Although it would be hard to lose the kittens, Sylvia felt sure she would be happier when they had gone to new homes, because the warehouse was full of machinery which could be lethal to the questing, curious scraps. Smudge was a good mother and did her best to keep them out of mischief, but it became more difficult as they got older. They were a handful and into everything.

Roland, a cheery lad of Jamaican parentage, called out a friendly greeting. He was very black with tight curly hair like a wire brush and a broad squat nose. Sylvia's first impression of him was that he was ugly. However, over the months, she had changed her mind. He was polite, nicely spoken and when he smiled his face was transformed. She remarked one day on how white his teeth were, and he told her that it came through chewing part of the bark of a tree. She didn't know whether to believe him.

He had already asked her to go to the pictures with him. She had refused and immediately felt sad when caught sight of his woe-begone face. But she was thinking of her parents' reaction if they knew she was going out with a 'Wog', as they called them! They were very prejudiced, mainly against black people and Jews. Her father had called Jews 'dirty rotten yids' when she had once mentioned that she quite liked Frankie Vaughan. She felt attracted to men with dark hair and brown eyes and had made up her mind to marry a man with those qualities.

"Hello, Roland," she said. "Have you seen Prudence today?"

He looked around and confessed that he hadn't; but he said the other kittens were roaming about.

Sylvia sat down on the wooden step and unwrapped her sandwiches, holding them out for him to share. He sat down beside her.

"I'm sorry, it's only spam and pickle," she said.

"They're lovely. Did you make them?"

In the background the wireless was playing the Everly Brothers' latest hit, 'Cathy's Clown', which reminded Sylvia at once of Prudence with her two teardrops. Hastily finishing her sandwiches and drinking her bottle of diluted orange squash, she set off to find the little kitten. She was about to drop her grease-proof paper into a dustbin she passed when, to her horror, she saw the little kitten lying dead on top of all the rubbish.

She screamed and rushed the whole length of the warehouse straight into the safety of Roland's arms.

"Hush!" he cried. "What on earth's the matter?"

"It's Prudence," she managed to stammer at last. "She's dead."

"Oh no! Surely not!"

"She is, she is. She's in that bin."

She led him, with tears pouring down her face, to the place. He could see at a glance that she was telling the truth.

"Come on," he said gently, picking up the tiny stiff body and placing it in a cardboard box, "we'll take it and give it a decent burial."

A heftily built man called Bert came hurrying up.

"Sorry, Sylvia," he said. "The poor little thing didn't stand a chance. It got trapped in the rollers and died almost instantly. It didn't suffer any pain. Me and Charlie were going to bury it, but the boss came down and nearly caught us, so we quickly threw it in the bin. We were going to bury it later. Honest!"

The boss didn't know that there was a warehouse cat, let alone kittens, so it was understandable that they should have reacted as they did. Sylvia felt, however, that it was an insult to toss something as beautiful as that in the bin.

"There's nowhere to bury it here. It's all concrete," she sobbed.

"I'll take it home with me," Roland volunteered. "I've a nice little garden in Camberwell where I live. It has a cherry tree which has beautiful blossoms in Spring. I think Prudence would like it there."

Inside the warehouse, Smudge was meowing plaintively, looking out for that missing one which would now never be found alive. She nosed into every corner, leaving nothing unturned, her cries growing stronger and more desperate.

Sylvia dropped to her knees and gathered the cat and the remaining kittens to her. Life was so cruel! She loved animals; she could understand them. She could remember going to the market on a Saturday to look at the puppies and kittens in the pet shop. It had made her upset, because she worried about what would happen to them when the shop shut for the weekend. Would they have food? Would they feel lonely? Her mother would see her crying and say that she was soppy. Trust her to be unsympathetic! She vowed then and there that one day, when she had married the dark-haired, brown-eyed man of her dreams, she would have a big house and all the animals that she could keep safe.

The next day, as they ate their sandwiches together, Roland told Sylvia that he had buried the kitten under the tree as promised. Perhaps she might like to come to his home at the weekend, he suggested, then she could see for herself?

Her first reaction was to refuse him, but then she thought of how kind he had been; and if she didn't tell her parents where she was going, they need never know. And what they didn't know, wouldn't hurt them, would it?

"I'd love to," she said, to his obvious surprise and delight.

He bubbled over with happiness and began telling her about his family. His mother was a nurse and his father worked as a driver on the buses. He had four brothers and three sisters, and they came from a poor part of Jamaica. Moving to England had transformed their lives. His mother was earning more over here in a week that she earned in a month back home. His father had also got a good job and made a decent wage by doing a lot of overtime.

Roland added: "I hope you will like West Indian cooking," and he smiled.

She assured him that she liked most food, with the exception of kippers and tea.

"That's funny," he remarked. "I thought all English people liked tea. My mother says they never do anything else except sit in each other's kitchens and drink tea!" he laughed at the thought of it.

Saturday came quickly. It was a typical June day with bright blue skies and warm sunshine. Sylvia had decided to ask Gloria if she could borrow the bike to cycle to Camberwell. She was quite proficient at riding it now, having overcome her fear of the London traffic. At first she had been very nervous of riding all the way from Peckham to the Old Kent Road, but the thought of the fares she saved made her persevere.

Gloria was naturally curious to know why she should want the bike at the weekend, so Sylvia found herself explaining about Roland. Gloria nodded; then she turned a critical eye on Sylvia's crumpled frock.

"Is that the best you could find?" she asked.

Sylvia pretended that she hadn't had time to iron it. The truth was, that she had to resort to copious lies in order to get out of the house without being found out.

"I can lend you one of mine," Gloria offered kindly.

"Oh, I couldn't."

"Oh, it's no trouble! Honestly! I've got masses of frocks that I hardly wear."

They found a frock of Gloria's that really did Sylvia justice. It was light green with a full flounced skirt and a stiffened petticoat underneath. The green complimented her eyes and her dark hair. She giggled at the thought of trying to ride a bike in it.

"I think I'd better catch the bus, after all," she said, "just to be on the safe side."

"Have you got enough money for the fare?"

"Thanks to you, yes! I manage to save quite a bit on fares now that I cycle to work. You really are a good friend," she said warmly, giving Gloria a peck on the cheek.

"Nonsense! That's what friends are for. Go on. Get going or you'll be late."

* * *

Sylvia sat on the upright kitchen chair, watching Mrs. Osborne flitting back and forth from the stove to the table, talking all the while. She had what was called a comfortable figure, but her face was broad, her nose squat and her voice deep. "Broad in the shoulders and warm in the heart," was how Roland described her.

Flinging a cloth over the table, she now turned to Roland and asked him to set the places. She addressed Sylvia.

"We always have our meals in the kitchen. I was going to open the dining room up, but you can go and sit in the front room if you want to. His dad will be home at ten past twelve on the dot – that is, if he hasn't been asked to work on. Well, he knows I put it on the table at the same time. If it's cold, that's his look-out. Would you like some tea while you're waiting?"

Sylvia, taken by surprised at being addressed so abruptly, stammered: "Yes . . . oh no! No, thank you! I can wait for my dinner."

Mrs. Osborne pushed out her ample chest, drew in her chin and, with a glance at Roland, thumbed towards Sylvia.

"She expects her dinner!" she said. "Did you hear that? She expects her dinner!"

Roland looked at Sylvia, whose face had turned scarlet. "Yes, she does, Mum," he said solemnly. "It's a blooming cheek, isn't it?"

Then they were both nearly killing themselves with laughter. The little woman came up and slapped Sylvia between the shoulders with such force that she coughed.

"Don't look so worried," she said. "I'm not going to eat you – not just yet, anyway."

Sylvia noticed the look that passed between mother and son. She remembered hearing someone say that black people ate humans when they lived in the

jungles of Africa, but felt sure it couldn't be true –
could it?

She managed to force a smile. Then, looking back at
Roland who was grinning at her, she bit on her lip and
moved her head slightly as if to say: "How am I going
to take her?"

Oscar Osborne was a thick-set man, broad rather
than tall; to Sylvia's eyes, he strangely resembled his
wife, at least in features. He was definitely not garru-
lous like her, however, as she soon found out. He
greeted Sylvia like one of the family with a nod and a
"Hello there!" followed by a conventional handshake
when they were introduced. Then he went to the sink
in the far corner of the kitchen to wash his hands;
coming back to the fireside to sit down in a chair to
the right of the oven, he watched his wife put out the
meal.

And what a meal it was! The small table was laden
with exotic food. Roland explained the various types
of dishes. There were Johnny cakes, made with batter,
yams and curry goat – which, he told her, was not goat
at all, but a special kind of West Indian meat. There
were pig tails made with a thick sauce, rice with black-
eyed peas, salt fish and a huge side salad.

"Come, girl! Eat hearty! You look as if you need fat-
tening up!" boomed Mrs. Osborne, as she placed
huge serving ladles in the dishes.

Sylvia couldn't remember when she had last
enjoyed a meal so much. She liked the spices and
thought of the bland food they had at home, which
was only livened up with the addition of tomato

ketchup or brown sauce with a sprinkling of salt and pepper. How horrified her parents would have been if they could have seen her sitting her enjoying a meal with the 'blacks'! She judged people by how they treated her. What did it matter what colour they were? The Osbornes were courteous and kindly and made her feel welcome. She would always be grateful to them for that.

Roland walked her to the bus stop. He fished in his pocket for some small change, which he offered to her.

"It's all right, thank you. I have some money of my own."

"Can I see you again?"

"I'd love to, but I don't think my parents would approve of our friendship."

"Well, don't tell them then."

"I can't keep lying to them; my mother is sure to find out."

He sighed. "Well, that's that then! I wish people wouldn't judge us by the colour of our skins."

"I don't." Sylvia put in hastily, and, not wanting to offend him, she arranged to meet him the next day. He had promised to take her to East Street Market in the Walworth Road. It meant more lies at home. Still, what the hell!

★　★　★

Sunday dawned grey and gloomy, in marked contrast to the previous day.

"Looks as if we're in for some rain," Mrs. Short

remarked at breakfast time. "And just where are you off to?"

"I thought I'd go to the Horniman Museum," lied Sylvia.

"Oh well. I suppose you'll at least be in the dry if it does rain. Who are you going with?"

"Just someone at work. You wouldn't know them," she added hastily to fend off more questions.

"Well . . . Still, if you've made arrangements to meet them, it's a bit late now to cancel. All right then," she grudgingly conceded.

"Thanks, Mother." Sylvia was grateful to have done with the cross examination. She wasn't a good liar. When she was younger and Mrs. Short had suspected her of telling lies, she had been made to put her tongue out. If her mother happened to see an ulcer on it, she would say that she had got it for telling lies. Sylvia, unfortunately, happened to get mouth ulcers regularly, whether she told lies or not!

She took her plastic rain mac and went to meet Roland.

He was waiting for her, looking out. As soon as he saw her coming, his face broke into a big grin showing his white teeth.

They boarded the bus which was to take them to East Street, and Sylvia was aware that they were attracting the attention of some of the other passengers. The Notting Hill race riots of 1958 were still fresh in everyone's minds. Then, gangs of young unemployed whites had terrorised any black people they saw on the streets, and relations had not improved much since. If a young white girl was seen in the company of a black man, she was likely to be called a "nigger lover". Sylvia, innocent as she was, was unaware of this and continued to enjoy the bus trip.

As they alighted, a watery sun peeped through the clouds, holding off the threatened rain. The stalls were colourful, and equally colourful characters were hawking their wares. The street was thronging with people. Some had simply come to look, while others were hopeful of a bargain. They stopped at a stall which sold sarsaparilla, a fruity drink. In the summer it was served cold and in winter, piping hot in glasses.

"Would you like a drink?" asked Roland. "It's really very nice."

"Yes, please."

He bought two plastic cups filled to the brim, and they wandered round the market, pausing occasionally to take a sip. Sylvia thought it wonderful. There were so many things to buy, and so cheap! She wondered why her mother never came here. A man was selling a fifty piece dinner and tea service for five shillings. Five shillings!

"Look!" she grabbed Roland's arms. "How on earth can he do that?"

The man selling the set had balanced plates all along his arm and was throwing the cups up in the air and catching them on his feet. Next he took two long sticks and, balancing a plate on each, whirled them giddily around on top.

Quite a crowd had gathered around his stall, and Sylvia expected at any moment to hear the crash of breaking china; but he appeared to be doing a good brisk trade.

At another place, she stopped to admire a frock. Roland immediately offered to buy it for her, but she refused; not because she didn't like it, but because she wouldn't be able to explain to her mother where it had come from.

They lost track of the time and only noticed that it was late when they saw the stallholders packing up to go home. Sylvia had had a lovely day and thanked Roland for taking her there. She longed to tell her mother about it and about the bargains that she could buy, but to do so would mean having to admit that she had lied about going to the Horniman Museum.

On the way home, Roland told her that his parents had liked her and hoped she would come for dinner again soon.

She said the feeling was mutual, but that she couldn't keep lying. Her mother always found out in the end.

"I do wish she wouldn't keep treating me like a baby," she told him. "I'm old enough to go to work, but she won't let me alone for a moment with her questions. She's on all the time about who I am going out with? Where am I going? What time will I be back?"

Roland shook his head, sympathising with her. They reached the top of Rye Lane, and it was time to part.

"Thank you once again for a simply lovely day! I really did enjoy myself! I wish I could take you home to meet my family, but I know they wouldn't approve," she said with regret. "Never mind! We can see each other at work and still be friends. That is, if you want to."

"Of course, I still want to. Hey, there's my bus!" he yelled, running towards it. He shouted back that he'd see her tomorrow. She watched as he threw himself on the moving bus and as it rounded the corner and bore him out of sight.

Chapter Twelve

Sylvia had been at David Rose's for nearly a year, and she had still not progressed beyond the office junior stage. She was tired of being the general dog's body, and saw no prospect for any improvement. One day as she was filling the urn for the umpteenth time, she decided that it was high time she looked for another job. She confided in Roland one lunchtime. They still met each other occasionally and were firm friends, nothing more.

"I'm fed up with this job. There's nothing for me here. Every day it's 'Do this, Miss Short! Do that, Miss Short!' I'm sick to death of it! I must get out before I go mad!"

Roland heaved a deep sigh. "Oh, Sylvia!" he said.

He turned away from her, thrusting his hands deep into his overall pockets. "I know your parents wouldn't approve of me. If your mother found out we were meeting, she would go mad, I realise that. Every time you want to see me you have to make some excuse, don't you, tell a lie of some sort? I hoped that one day we could meet openly instead of sneaking around. It's killing me inside when I mostly see you at work. Don't go, please! I . . . I love you, Sylvia. Looking back, I can't remember a time when I didn't love you. Do . . . do you love me?"

She kept her head lowered, not daring to meet his eyes, and her words were hardly audible above the noise of the machinery in the warehouse as she replied: "What's the good of loving someone you . . . you can never have?"

"But . . . but you can! I don't care what your parents think, or anyone else for that matter. I'd marry you tomorrow if you'd have me. Will you Sylvia?"

She lifted her head then and looked at him. Yes, she did like him, she liked him a lot. Perhaps she even loved him – she didn't know.

"Look, Roland, I've got to go." she put out her hand as if to ward him off. "I'm late already."

"You don't care for me? You don't even like me?"

"Don't be silly." She took a step towards him. "You know I like you. But I'm not ready yet for what you want. I don't want to be tied down to anyone. I do like you, Roland, really I do. Don't be in any doubt about that!"

"But you don't love me?" His voice was flat.

"Look, I've got to go now. Bye-bye." She backed away two steps from him, then turned and ran up the stairs.

He did not try to follow.

She gave in her notice that afternoon. She had decided that it would be best all round. She didn't think she was being fair to Roland, and staying there would serve as a constant reminder of something they both knew could never happen. She was to leave in two weeks and she had reckoned that she would find another job during that time. She was reminded that she would receive the week's salary that was owed to her from when she had begun. It would tide her mother over until she found another job.

★ ★ ★

It almost seemed to Sylvia that Mrs. Short had been waiting behind the hall door for her; because no sooner had she entered the house than there she was, glowering at her.

"I want you in the living room a moment," she said.

Sylvia raised her eyebrows. What was all this about? She was not left long in doubt. Mrs. Short followed her into the room, closed the door and then stood with her back to it, her normally pale face tinged to a deep red.

"Think you're smart, don't you?" she cried, thrusting out her chin. "Lying, sneaking, crawling individual that you've become! And all to see that black boy! Well, it's finished. Do you hear? You attempt to go near him again and I'll make it my business to go across there . . ."

"Shut up!"

Sylvia's patience had finally snapped.

Mrs. Short nearly choked with surprise. The colour deepened in her face and her breath seemed to have become laboured as Sylvia went on:

"You'll not tell me any more what I've got to do and what I haven't got to do. I'm sick and tired of your domination. Do you hear? Do you hear me? If I want to see Roland, then I'll see Roland, in spite of you or anyone else. Do you hear me?"

Mrs. Short found her voice again, her face becoming so suffused with anger that it seemed to send out rays of heat.

"Yes, I hear you!" she cried. "And now you hear me. I'm your mother and I forbid you to take that tone with me. And you dare to tell me to shut up – me?"

"Mother?" Sylvia flung back scornfully. "You call yourself my mother? Huh! You have made it quite clear to me over the years what your feelings are for me. You have denied me a mother's love. All you're interested in is how much money I bring you at the end of each week! Well, let me make it plain. I intend to get another job. Yes!" she went on fiercely. "And when I do, I mean to give you what I think you need – what I shall decide! I shall buy myself some new clothes like other people. I shall enjoy myself like other people. I will not be scared of you anymore. And how did you find out about Roland anyway? No, don't tell me, let me guess! One of your so-called friends! Well, it's none of their business what I do, and as from now, it's none of yours."

Sylvia felt drained after this outburst, but the effect on her mother was more dire. She watched her lean against the door, her body sagging, her eyes closed. She suddenly looked old. She was only forty-seven, but at that moment she could have been an old woman.

Mrs. Short's fury seemed spent, but not her spite. When she spoke again, it was in a low ominous voice.

"Get out! Get out of this house and never come back. Do you hear?"

Sylvia had not expected this, although she wasn't altogether surprised.

"Where shall I go?"

"I really don't care. You have made it perfectly clear that what you do is none of my business. Leave my house. Now!"

Sylvia took the stairs two at a time, her mind racing. She forced herself to stay calm and think rationally. Money! She must have money! She emptied the coins out of the gin bottle and counted them. It came to four pounds and sixpence. Hardly a fortune! Maybe it would be enough for a room for a couple of weeks until she finished her job at David Rose. Or perhaps one of her friends would put her up. Gloria? Veronica?

Her thoughts were interrupted as her mother entered the bedroom and flung a battered suitcase onto the bed.

"You can have this for your rubbish," she said

nastily. "Hurry up! I can hardly wait to see the back of you."

Sylvia felt her own anger building up inside her, but she did not reply, although there was plenty more she could have said. She threw what few clothes she had into the case, brushed past her mother and went down the stairs, out of the front door and into the street. Mrs. Short's parting words would ring in her ears for ever more:

"I hate you! I hate you with every breath in my body, until the day I die!"

* * *

Footsore and weary, Sylvia sank down into some bushes at the top end of Peckham Rye park, out of sight of prying eyes. Darkness was falling and all around her were the eerie sounds of the night. She was alone and afraid. Since leaving her house she had called on several friends to see if they would give her a room for the night. Each one had given her the same answer: "Sorry. No room!" Now she knew how Mary and Joseph must have felt when they were turned away from the inn!

Tomorrow would be better, she promised herself. First thing in the morning she would go into work and explain the situation. With that, she fell into a troubled sleep.

When she awoke the first light of morning was lacing the sky. She had no idea of the time, but she guessed it was early as the streets were still quiet apart from an occasional chink of milk bottles on a float, driven by the milkman. She yawned and stretched, rubbing some life back into her limbs. Her clothes were crumpled, her hair a mess. She made for the nearest toilet and washed, dressed and put on a change of clothes. Then, satisfied that she looked more presentable, she set off through the park for the bus stop.

As she sat on a wall, waiting for a bus, she tried to think of what she was going to do next. It was all very well to assert her independence, but what did that amount to if she had nowhere to live? She couldn't keep carrying this suitcase around for ever. The first bus that showed up was going to the Old Kent Road. The kindly conductor who came to take her fare, stared at her.

"What's a nice girl like you doing up so early in the morning?" he said. "Can't wait to get to work, eh?"

"I didn't sleep very well last night," she replied truthfully.

Arriving at work, she found the gates locked. She sat down and waited for what seemed an eternity. She must have dozed off; then a voice woke her.

"Good God! You look awful!" It was Roland.

Sylvia got to her feet, rubbing her eyes. "Oh, Roland," she cried, suddenly despairing, "I don't know what to do!"

"I'll make you a cup of coffee and then you can tell me all about it. Here, let me take that." He put out a hand for her suitcase.

The coffee refreshed Sylvia and she found herself

spilling out the whole story of her woes to Roland, who listened patiently.

"I'd offer to let you stay at our house, but we're overcrowded as it is," he told her.

"I know you are," she said, biting her bottom lip. "Anyway, it's the thought that counts. No, I'll have to sort it out in my own way – but thanks all the same."

When the manager arrived, Sylvia asked the girl on reception if she could see him for a moment. She then repeated her story to him, but he told her there was nothing he could do. He already knew that she was leaving, so he felt it was none of his concern. Now, if she had not been leaving . . . He was not indifferent, however, and offered to waive the two weeks notice by giving her her wages now, along with the first weeks' wage which was due to her. That ought to help her to find some accommodation, he said.

She was suitably grateful; then asked if she would be able to leave her case there while she was looking around. He agreed. They shook hands as a parting gesture.

She had decided against seeing Roland. She knew he would only worry about her and she didn't feel up to answering any more of his questions.

All that day, she scoured London for accommodation. She looked younger than her sixteen years and people seemed to view her with suspicion. After a while, she began to get used to doors being slammed shut on her, and then curtains being twitched as opinions were voiced as to whether she was a runaway. As evening set in once again, she found herself at Kings Cross Station. Nothing had been achieved.

Tired and disillusioned, she sat on a wooden bench and studied the timetables that were displayed on the board. Over the tannoy, a disembodied voice announced that the next train to depart from platform two was the ten-fifty to Blackpool. Blackpool! She had never been there before. Who was to say that she had to stay in London? Checking her money carefully, she decided that she had more than enough to pay for a ticket.

She found herself in a corner seat in a carriage and curled up and put her coat over her. As the train clattered along the tracks, she swore she could hear it saying: "Blackpool, Blackpool . . . ."

She awoke suddenly to find that it was still quite dark. The train rolled into the station at Lytham St Anne's; she remembered from the notice board at Kings Cross that Blackpool was the next stop. What a fool she had been not to bring her suitcase with her! Never mind, she had a little money which could be used to buy a change of clothes.

"Blackpool! This is Blackpool! All change, please!"

She glanced at the clock in the station. It was a quarter to five in the morning. She was astonished to see so many people; she was quite jostled as she moved along with the throng. Everyone looked busy and most had someone to meet them. She felt alone and quite forlorn. There would be no-one waiting for her. Nobody knew where she was – and nobody cared.

* * *

Sylvia spent all her money in that first week, on a change of clothes and food. In her second week in Blackpool, she went hungry; she was tired and very cold. It was not so bad in the day when the sun came out; but the nights were cold, even for August. She had managed to find a safe place to sleep under the pier. But if it rained, it made a poor shelter and the drips from the wooden planks overhead thoroughly soaked her. She had gone to the labour exchange to try to get a job, but when they saw the state she was in and how she stank, she was shown the door. She also went to the Social Security to plead with them for some money.

"I'm afraid we can't help you without an accommodation address." said the snooty young lady at the desk.

"But . . . how can I get an address when you won't give me any money to find a place to live?"

"That, I'm afraid, is your problem," the girl told her.

And so Sylvia had no alternative but to go back to her retreat under the pier. That same night she was rudely awoken by someone shining a torch on her face and a loud voice enquiring: "What have we here then?" Still half asleep, she felt herself being pulled roughly to her feet.

"Take your arms away and let's have a look at you."

"Please," she said, blinking a couple of times, "could you stop shining that torch in my eyes?"

The policeman's gruff manner turned to one of concern when he saw how young she was.

"I think I'd better take you back to the station. "It's

all right," he added, noticing her frightened look, "I won't bite you. Have you run away from home then?"

She shook her head wearily.

"All right. We'll have a nice little chat later when you have had something to eat. Hungry, are you?"

She nodded. She was so tired that she couldn't think of anything else to say.

At the station, she was given a meal before being handed over to a WPC, a friendly woman who said that her name was Mary, and that Sylvia mustn't be scared as they were only trying to help. By now, Sylvia was sobbing. Why couldn't they understand that she didn't feel like talking now? Maybe tomorrow . . .

The WPC said: "Is it all right, Sarge, if I take her home with me? I suspect she needs a good bath and a good night's sleep?"

The station sergeant scratched his head. "I dunno about that, Mary. She should be in custody until we've decided what's gonna be done about her."

"I'll personally see to it that she comes back with me in the morning. She hardly looks like a criminal, does she?"

"Well," said the sergeant doubtfully, "If you're sure."

Sylvia felt a lot better after a hot bath. She dried herself with a big fluffy towel and slipped into a pair of winceyette pyjamas that were so large that they threatened to swamp her. She drank a bowl of soup that Mary had heated up on the stove, but she shook her head at the offer of sausage, egg and beans. Her stomach didn't feel up to it.

The WPC tucked her up in a huge bed in the back bedroom, and for the first time in weeks Sylvia slept like a baby.

The next morning, she managed a lightly boiled egg and a slice of bread and butter. Mary was sympathetic, and Sylvia found herself opening up to her and telling her about her home and her adopted parents.

Back at the station, it was decided that she should be returned to London and placed in care of the Welfare there. Her case was complicated by the fact that she was only sixteen and therefore, in the eyes of the law, only a minor.

Mary accompanied her on the train as far as Kings Cross. There she was handed over to a worker from Lambeth Welfare Offices and taken to Crystal Palace Road Police Station. Guided by the Welfare Officer, she then made a sworn statement concerning her father's sexual abuse of her. The harrowing story provoked anger amongst even the toughest policeman.

While a case was being prepared, Sylvia, through no fault of her own, was placed in a remand home in South Norwood, there being no other accommodation available for her. Some of the other girls at the home were already hardened young criminals and she suffered at their hands.

"What are you in 'ere for, then?" they demanded.

"Nothing really."

"'Ark at 'er! 'Nuffink', she says. Miss Goody Goody. Let's get 'er, girls!"

They were like wild things, biting and scratching; one even went so far as to hit her with an empty coke bottle. Sylvia complained to the staff, who didn't seem to be in the least bit interested, and this only earned her a further beating from the girls, who claimed she had grassed them up.

One girl in particular singled out Sylvia to make her life a misery. This girl was the 'top-dog' and commanded respect from the others. She was a fat, ugly, masculine looking girl called Bertha. Bert would have been a more appropriate name for her. She had a tattoo on the side of her neck; a skull with the word 'KILL' written in bold lettering across the skeletal face. All the other inmates used to call her Mad Bertha. She was an evil and thoroughly spiteful girl, who would stop at nothing to get her own way. She had her band of followers who were at her beck and call, night and day. They pandered to her every whim. Not because they particularly liked her, but because they were afraid of her and the power she had among the staff. Mad Bertha had 'friends' inside and outside who would smuggle in cigarettes, alcohol and worse still . . . drugs.

For some reason, Mad Bertha was jealous of Sylvia and this made her even more determined to make the girl's life a misery.

*　*　*

One night, after lights were out and gentle snores could be heard throughout the dormitory, one person lay awake hatching a plan. Mad Bertha giggled spitefully. Creeping out of bed, she tiptoed across to rouse some of her cronies. Whispering together in the corner of the room they made their plans to sort out Sylvia once and for all!

The next evening started out quietly enough. Some of the inmates were watching television in the recreation room. Others were playing a game of snooker. But Sylvia sat alone in the corner reading a book. Mad Bertha watched her, an evil smile playing across her lips. Catching the attention of Molly and Joan, she inclined her head in the direction of Sylvia, and then made a gesture to the door behind her. Quick to catch on the two of them casually ambled over to Sylvia.

"Wotcha reading then?" asked Molly companionably.

"Just a book." replied Sylvia

"Yeah, we can see that. But wot's it about?" asked Joan.

Then, not waiting for answer, they put their plan into action.

"Fancy coming to the library to help me choose a book?" Molly enquired.

"You can't even read you dummy." sniggered Joan.

"Course I can you idiot!" Molly retorted.

Sylvia watched the pair of them guardedly. She felt sure something was amiss.

"Well. Are you coming with me or not?" demanded Molly.

Sylvia rose to her feet. Trying to force a smile to hide her nervousness, she allowed herself to be led from the room sandwiched between the two of them.

Once outside the recreation room, all pleasantries

disappeared. Instead of turning left along the corridor, which would have taken them to the library, they turned right which took them to the shower room. Making sure that no one had followed them, they pushed Sylvia roughly inside. Sylvia fell across the floor with gasp of pain, momentarily winded. Molly and Joan grabbed her arms and began to fasten them behind her back with a length of rope. While she was still lying on the floor unable to get up, they proceeded also to bind her legs together with another length of rope. Sylvia opened her mouth to scream.

"Don't you dare try that!" warned Molly, stuffing a dirty wet cloth in the girls mouth that she'd found next to the lavatory. Sylvia gagged against it. The bile reached her mouth, but had no escape. A shadow stepped from one of the cubicles, but before Sylvia could see who the shadow belonged to she was turned roughly over so that she was now lying face down on the floor.

"Roll up her sleeve!" hissed a voice, urgently.

Sylvia felt a sharp pain in the top of her arm. She tried to turn round. A boot dug into the back of her neck preventing her. She felt something trickling over her head and down her back. It smelt like . . . it smelt like . . . her father! She blacked out.

* * *

"What have you done? She's dead!" Joan wailed.

"Pull yourself together." snapped Bertha. "She's only having a little sleep, that's all. Here, help me untie these ropes. Who tied these ropes?" she demanded. "They're too tight! I told you not to leave any marks. Didn't I? Didn't I?" she screamed through clenched teeth. "You're both so stupid. I ought to . . ."

Molly and Joan backed away fearfully.

"Don't worry. I'm not going to hurt you . . . Just get those ropes untied. Now!"

They worked quickly and quietly. Then they pulled Sylvia into a cubicle and propped her against the lavatory with her head lolling over the pan.

"What do we do now?" asked Joan.

Mad Bertha scratched her head.

"Yes. What do we do now?" echoed Molly.

"Oh for goodness sake, stop asking questions. Can't you see I'm trying to think!" Bertha replied. After a while, she threw her head back and laughed. "I know what!"

"What?"

"You two stay here with her. I'll go and find someone. Tell them that we came in here for a piss and found her lying in the toilet. They'll naturally assume that she's drunk smelling like that. She must have gone to the toilet to be sick and then . . . passed out!"

By the time Bertha came back with a member of staff, Sylvia had started to come round.

They helped her to her feet and back into the dormitory. Too groggy to undress herself, Bertha assisted her, making certain that the pin prick from the needle which contained the heroin was not visible. Her eyes bored into Sylvia's. Sylvia got the message. She mustn't say anything to implicate this evil woman and her cronies, for her punishment could be fatal next time.

The next day when Sylvia was hauled before the governor to explain her actions of the previous night, she agreed that had she had been offered a drink which had affected her badly. This explanation was accepted without question, although not without further punishment to Sylvia for disobeying the rules. She was not allowed to use either the library or recreation room for the rest of her stay. She was also confined to a solitary room and not allowed any contact with the others. To Sylvia, this was a relief as it meant that the bullying would stop, although she wasn't too happy about going without her reading materials. Books were her life and her escapism. Fortunately the dose of heroin which she had been given was such a small amount that it had no lasting effects, apart from Sylvia experiencing a slight touch of hallucination during the night.

★　★　★

After nearly a week of this misery, the Welfare Officer came and told her that a court hearing had been set for the following Friday at Lambeth Juvenile Court. Sylvia thought with horror that another week in this place would be the death of her, and she told Miss Wilson as much.

"I know you shouldn't be here, but we don't have anywhere else to put you," the woman said apologetically. "I'm looking for something more suitable, but it's not easy . . ." She raised her hands helplessly.

Sylvia bravely managed to endure a further week without too many mishaps thanks to being placed back in solitary confinement, but she could still feel the other girls' hostility towards her when she was let out for an hour a day for her exercise. Although she had no direct contact with any of the other inmates now, it didn't stop them from shouting down to her while she was taking her walk around the square. They thought she was different, stuck up.

"Good riddance!" they shouted, when the car came to take her to court. Don't bother coming back here. We don't want you!"

"No! And I don't want to come back here," thought Sylvia, shuddering inwardly, as the car drew away from the drab grey building, with it's barred windows and locked doors.

Chapter Thirteen

At Lambeth Juvenile Court there was a delay, and finally it was announced that the hearing could not proceed as neither of Sylvia's parents had turned up. Sylvia, to her dismay, found herself being escorted back to the remand home for another week!

She burst into tears at the thought of seeing those awful girls again, and told Miss Wilson that she would prefer to go anywhere other than that place.

Miss Wilson's heart went out to her. It was, she said, a most unfortunate situation and she only wished that there were something she could do. If only she had her way, she would have taken Sylvia home with her, but that was quite impossible.

"We'll find something better for you, I'm sure of

that," she said. "When the court case is over, I'll make certain that more appropriate accommodation is found."

Sylvia spent another awful week at the remand home. She held her head high, determined not to let the taunts and threats get to her. She kept reassuring herself that it was not for much longer. How she hoped her parents would turn up for the next hearing. She didn't think she could stand much more of this!

This time however, she was not put into solitary confinement, and had to endure further bullying from 'Mad Bertha' and her cronies who were delighted to see their 'little friend'. Fortunately the episode of the heroin was not repeated, although she was subjected to icy cold showers in the middle of the night.

Friday finally came and she arrived at the court in a state of high anxiety. She was relieved to see her mother sitting outside court number one and went over to speak to her. Mrs. Short turned her head away. Sylvia felt various emotions sweep over her – bitterness, hurt and anger. In a fit of rage, she cried aloud:

"Don't worry, you'll never see me again . . . ever!"

Still her mother looked away. She never said a word.

Sylvia walked back and rejoined Miss Wilson, who told her that she would be going in very shortly and to tell the judge what had happened to her in her own words.

"They're not here to punish you, Sylvia," she said, "only to get the facts as they happened. Don't be frightened of them. They only have your best interests at heart."

The case took one and a half hours, during which time all sides of the story were aired. Mrs. Short looked genuinely shocked at some of the more harrowing details, although she managed to remain composed. Her husband, however, was a different matter. He maintained an outward calm and dismissed the charges against him as a bundle of lies. He said that Sylvia had made the whole story up to get back at them in some way.

"We have always done our best for her," he whined. "Why, if we hadn't come along, she would still be in a foster home. We gave her love and cared for her as if she were our own. Now look how she repays us! I think she must be sick to invent such stories."

It was her word against his, but there were others brought forward to add their voices. Neighbours told of how they had suspected that all was not right in the house, and how, on a couple of occasions, they had even called the NSPCC when Sylvia had been heard screaming after a particularly severe beating.

The court chairman gave his summing up, and he was scrupulously fair. He said he hoped the jury now felt they were in possession of all the facts; it was up to them to decide if the girl was a pathological liar capable of making up lies to hurt this family who had adopted her – and, if she was, to ask themselves what would be the benefit of her doing so. Or had the father taken advantage of her vulnerability and innocence to vent his perverted sexual desires upon her?

The jury retired for an hour. When they returned, their decision was unanimous: Mr. Short was undoubtedly guilty! There was a sudden commotion in the court as Mrs. Short rose to her feet.

"It's her who's the liar!" she screamed. "Can't you see what she's doing to us?" She turned to Sylvia. "I hope you rot in hell! You're evil through and through! . . . " She would have said more, but an officer of the court interfered and led her outside.

The chairman proceeded to pass his verdict.

"This court does not have the power to send you to prison. Therefore I am going to remand you in custody to be sent for trial at the High Court." he told the prisoner. "I hope you will have time to reflect upon the seriousness of your crimes. I shall arrange for you to receive psychiatric help during your stay and you will of course, be placed in a special wing for your own safety. Prisoners don't take kindly to child molesters."

Mr. Short, visibly shaken, was helped down the stairs from the dock to a cell below, to await transport to Brixton Prison.

When Sylvia saw her mother being escorted from the court, her head bent low and tears in her eyes, she felt an intense pity for her family. She had never for one moment dreamt that it would end like this. Yet she knew that they hated her . . . but why? Why couldn't they have been like a proper family? Where had she gone wrong? What had she done to make them despise her so? All unanswered questions!

"Come along, dear," said Miss Wilson, holding out

her hand. "The chairman wants to see you in his office."

Mr. Watts smiled at the girl. "There now," he said, "It's all over. No-one is ever going to hurt you like that again. Has Miss Wilson told you where you are going? No? Well, she has found a place for you in Blackheath with some other children. No, it's not what you think," he went on, noticing Sylvia's look of distress. "These children are a lot younger than you, and I daresay you can help some of the staff look after them. Unfortunately, there is a lack of homes for girls your age, but I'm sure you will settle down given time; and when something more suitable is found for you, you will be moved accordingly. "I'm sure the time will come when you will look back on all this and laugh. Meanwhile, I wish you all the luck for the future. Have you any questions you wish to ask me?"

Sylvia then asked a surprising thing. "When will I be allowed to go home again?"

"When the time is right, my dear; when the time is right."

★   ★   ★

Mrs. Short returned to the family home alone, to be met on all sides with black looks and accusing stares. The neighbours had read about the case in the South London Press and were shocked and sickened by what they had learned. They had an inkling that Sylvia was being mistreated, but sexually assaulted as well . . .

Mrs. Short tried to go about her daily business as normal. She held her head high as she strutted off to Rye Lane to get the weekly shopping. She nodded to a passing acquaintance, who stared through her as if she were a piece of dirt. She stopped at Home and Colonial to buy some cheese and luncheon meat. Veronica's mother was in the queue and although the two women had never met, she recognised her from the picture in the local paper. She marched angrily over to Sylvia's mother and in a loud voice told her in no uncertain terms just what she thought of her. Mrs. Short could have died of shame. All the customers in the shop were staring at her. She started to speak . . .

"I'm really very sorry, but do I know you?"

Veronica's mother glared at her. "No, you don't know me, but I know all about you and your husband. Read it in the paper. Disgusting business if you ask me."

Mrs. Short glowered at her. "I'm not asking you. My business is nothing to do with you, or anyone else for that matter. Yes, that goes for all of you." She glared at the shop full of customers defying them to answer her back.

Mrs. Coles continued. " I am one of those people you look down on. Yes . . . look down on! I live in a prefab, so that makes me a gypsy in your eyes doesn't it? Sylvia came to our house many times to play with our daughter when they were at primary school together. I always thought it strange that she never stayed for tea or to invite Veronica back to play with her. I kept hoping that we would meet so that I could introduce myself and assure you that my intentions towards Sylvia were meant kindly. I even toyed with the idea of coming round to visit you. That was until I overheard from one of your neighbours what you were really like. Do you want to know what she called you? No? Well I'll tell you anyway. She called you a stuck up snobby bitch. You with your fur coats and high handed attitude. I'll bet you haven't even got a pot to piss in!"

Mrs. Short gave a gasp of horror. "You wicked woman! It's no wonder I don't want to let my daughter get involved with the likes of you!"

"Daughter! Daughter, you say? You don't even deserve to call her your daughter after the dreadful way you and your husband have abused her. Poor little mite. If I'd have known what you two were doing to her, I'd have taken her in myself. How can the adoption society justify themselves when they are dealing with the likes of you. Thoroughly vetted so they say. Have to be a Christian and go to church . . . so they say. All that red tape, and for what . . .? Makes you think doesn't it? I'm glad I didn't have to give a child up for adoption. I'd never forgive myself if I knew it was going to so-called parents like you. It's all show as far as you're concerned. You didn't even want her."

By now the crowd in the shop were thoroughly enjoying the scene being acted out before them.

Mrs. Coles took a step forward as if to hit the other woman, then thought better of it. "No – you're not worth getting into trouble for. Look at her now the stupid bitch!" She gestured her thumb towards Mrs. Short who was by now edging her way shamefacedly to the door, all thoughts of the shopping forgotten.

"Let me tell you one thing," she screeched after her. "I wouldn't spit on you if you were dying of thirst, you miserable wretch!"

With those words ringing in her ears Mrs. Short abandoned her shopping trip and came home.

She sent John out to run the errands as she didn't dare show her face outside the door for fear of being attacked.

John didn't mind, but he was worried about his mother. After three weeks indoors and two letters from his father, which had gone unanswered, he told her that she must pull herself together.

"Why?" came the curt reply.

"Because it won't do you any good to keep hiding all the time, that's why. All I ever see you do is peer behind the curtains. You've had them closed for over a fortnight. People will think that someone has died."

"Someone has." said his mother forlornly.

"Oh for goodness sake," said John exasperately, "go and see Mrs. Johnson. I'm sure she'll still be talking to you. Anyway, I think it's all blown over by now. You know what they say about todays news? That tomorrow it will be history. And why haven't you written to Dad?"

"Can't think of anything to say to him." snapped Mrs. Short.

"You don't believe Sylvia, do you?"

"I don't know what to believe anymore." This last

remark was uttered on a long drawn out sigh. Nevertheless, she got up and fetched her cardigan, then went and knocked on Mrs. Johnson's door.

Winnie was shocked at how much her neighbour had aged in the short space of time since she had last seen her. She was reluctant to ask her in, but mindful of what others might think if they saw her talking to her on the doorstep, she proceeded to open the door further to allow her inside.

Over a cup of tea the whole story poured forth from Mrs. Short. She talked without hardly pausing for breath. About how she couldn't have children and the fact that if she adopted children it would get her out of doing the dreaded war work. On and on it flowed like a never ending stream. Finally she said to June's mother:

"I wish I had the time all over again, to say that I'm sorry to Sylvia. I wanted to love her, but I just couldn't."

June's mother felt very sad as she let Mrs. Short out of the back gate. Whether it was Mrs. Short she felt sorry for or Sylvia, she wasn't sure. It made her feel glad about her own happy little family and she told her husband Wilf as much when he came home from work that evening. Wilf pulled her to him, told her how much he loved her and did she fancy an early night. Giggling like a young schoolgirl, she allowed her husband to carry her upstairs, where they showed their love for each other in that quiet way that adults sometimes have.

Mrs. Short came back home and sat in the armchair

feeling quite unwell. She took to her bed soon after and never rose from it again. She had three heart attacks, one after the other, and died. So the bitter words that Sylvia had flung at her inside the court came true. The questions that Sylvia had asked herself would now remain locked away forever . . . .

* * *

Sylvia did her best to settle into her new surroundings in a large Victorian children's home on the edge of Blackheath. She was not told of her mother's death until she received a letter from John two weeks after the funeral. When Miss Wilson came to visit her, she asked why she had been kept in ignorance. Miss Wilson replied that she had not known herself until quite recently, and she felt that Sylvia had undergone enough upheaval during the past few weeks, without having to cope with this extra shock. She had intended to tell her in time.

Sylvia felt her world had been turned upside down. She wished she had not said those hurtful words at the time of their last meeting. In some way, she now felt responsible for her mother's death and inconsolable with grief. Later that night, when all was quiet, she packed her few belongings and ran away. She was found living rough under the arches in Peckham Rye Station, and was taken back to Blackheath.

"What on earth are we going to do with you?" Miss Wilson said, shaking her head.

Sylvia mumbled that she didn't know.

Following discussions at the Welfare Office, it was decided to place her at Shirley Oaks in Croydon. This was a hostel for older girls, and it was felt that Sylvia would settle down better with girls of her own age. The experiment was not a success. Sylvia found the same sort of bullying went on as in the remand centre. Again she ran away; again she was found and brought back. This time the department decided to send her outside London and a place was found for her in Upper Portslade, just outside Brighton.

Miss Wilson came to collect her in a battered old Morris Minor and soon they were speeding through the country lanes. The woods bordering the roads were thick, the dwellings sparse. Here and there Sylvia caught glimpses of fields and hills beyond the trees. The dullness of the day matched the dullness in her heart.

Soon the car pulled into a driveway, passing through large, ornate gates into a long gravelled lane which was in need of some repair. The gardens on each side, after a brief expanse of woodland, were mainly laid to lawn. Then the house reared up, imposing in its greyness and bleakness. Sylvia hated it from the moment she saw it.

Miss Wilson brought the car to a halt below a short flight of stone steps that led up to Loxdale's entrance. A woman was waiting at the door to meet them, her face grim and unwelcoming. Miss Wilson extended a hand to introduce herself, while Sylvia still dallied by the car, collecting her luggage, and delaying the moment when she must enter the house. She climbed the steps and the woman held one half of the double door open, the daylight revealing her grey hair and lined face.

It took a while for Sylvia's eyes to adjust to the gloom of the cavernous hallway. The shadows were thick here and the oak panelling, which covered most of the walls, added it's own sombreness.

They were shown into an office lined with bookshelves and grey, chest-high filing cabinets. A desk, its top cluttered with documents, journals and reference books, faced a door that was ajar. A smaller desk, equally untidy, took up a space near a corner. It was a room crammed with the written word but, at that moment, empty of life. After a brief exchange of notes and a hasty cup of tea, Miss Wilson departed, leaving Sylvia to the mercy of the unsmiling woman.

Sylvia and Miss Morrison stood looking at each other for what seemed an interminable time. Finally the woman spoke.

"You will address me as Miss Morrison at all times. You will not speak unless you are spoken to. You will be expected to keep your room clean and help around the house, and you will of course go to work. Is that clear?"

"Yes."

"Yes, what?"

"Yes, Miss Morrison."

"That's better! Now, you can ask me any questions that you may have. Come along, girl!"

"Do you think it would be possible for me to work in an office?"

The laugh was thin and dry, like crackling bones.

"An office! An office! Are you joking?"

Sylvia assured her that she wasn't.

"Well, I'm sorry to inform you that all my girls go to work in Greens Sponge Mixture Factory. The management there do not worry about your various backgrounds and will take anyone on without question. You seem to have very high falutin' ways, Miss!"

Sylvia felt her eyes begin to prick with the threat of tears.

"I am not a number," she said fiercely, "nor am I one of your girls! My name is Sylvia Short and I don't want to work in your rotten old factory!"

"We'll see about that."

The woman grabbed her roughly by the arm and practically dragged her up the stairs to a tiny, dingy bedroom.

"You can stay here until you learn some manners," she snapped, flinging her suitcase on the bed. "It's useless to try and beat the system. You will go to the factory tomorrow. In fact, I shall take you there myself." With that she spun on her heel and walked out of the bedroom without a backward glance.

"Oh my God, what have I let myself in for this time?" thought Sylvia, gazing about her. The furniture was sparse and well worn. The bed looked clean enough until she pulled back the sheets and saw with dismay that the mattress was covered with stains. She shuddered at the thought of sleeping on it, but eventually she crept between the sheets and dozed fitfully until morning.

A bell rang somewhere, jerking her awake. She went out onto the landing where she encountered a small group of other girls. They greeted her politely enough, but all talk stopped when Miss Morrison was heard coming up the stairs.

"Ah! Good! At least you don't have to be called half a dozen times to get up. Hurry up and get washed, then I'll take you to Green's."

An audible groan could be heard and Miss Morrison's head twitched round sharply.

"Who made that noise? Own up?"

No one uttered a word.

"Very well. I shall find out who the culprit is, and when I do they will be punished. Make no mistake about that!"

Sylvia sat quietly on the bus next to Miss Morrison. She could see the sea out of the window. How she loved the sea! Maybe . . . just maybe, she could settle down here.

"Come along. We get off here. Quickly now!"

Miss Morrison smile ingratiatingly at the male supervisor.

This is Sylvia, who has come to live with our happy family. Haven't you dear?" she added encouragingly, nodding at Sylvia, who merely inclined her head.

The supervisor cleared his throat and absentmindedly rubbed his nose.

"Ah! Well, I think we can find a place for you.

"Jennifer!" he called to a girl standing nearby. "Take Sylvia through to the bicarbonate of soda, will you? Show her what to do and I'll be along presently."

Sylvia found herself sitting on a tall wooden stool, mesmerised by the tins of bicarbonate of soda which came whizzing past her eyes. Her job, she found out, was simply to apply a top to each one as they came by. "God, this is stupid!" she thought, and was really pleased when the whistle blew at the end of the day. On the bus she got talking with some others from Loxdale and heard them calling Miss Morrison a witch.

"She's really awful, don't you think?" a pretty fair-haired girl asked her.

"I don't really know her yet," Sylvia confessed, "but if she's as nasty as she was yesterday, then yes, I do think she's awful!"

That night, Sylvia began to think about running away again. She simply could not stand another day doing such a monotonous job. As for Loxdale, well, it was no home for her. She had no idea where she would go or what she would do, she only knew she had to get away.

At lunchtime the next day she confided in Beryl, the fair-haired girl, who begged her to take her with her.

"I couldn't do that," Sylvia told her. "It could get you into a lot of trouble."

"Please!"

Beryl was as determined as she was, so Sylvia reluctantly agreed. The two girls slipped out of Loxdale and hitched a lift to London.

Chapter Fourteen

It was only a matter of days before they were found. Tired, dirty and bedraggled, they had to face the wrath of the Lambeth Social Services Department. Beryl was promptly despatched to Loxdale. As for Sylvia . . .

"Dear child, what on earth are we going to do with you?" sighed Miss Wilson. "You can't keep running away whenever the fancy takes you. Look at the state of you! What have you got to say for yourself?"

Sylvia shrugged and peered down moodily at her feet.

"Very well. We're going to try you in a new home that has just opened in St. Paul's Cray. That's near Orpington in Kent, you know."

Sylvia didn't know and nor did she particularly care. Her mood changed drastically, however, when she saw the home. It was set in lovely grounds, was brand new and, to top it all, she had a choice of bedrooms as she was the first girl there. She chose one which looked out over woodlands. If she peered closely, she could see a family of rabbits. The walls of the room were papered with tiny rosebuds and the furniture was painted a delicate shade of pale pink.

"It's lovely!" she breathed.

"Well, make sure you stay here," grunted Miss Wilson, who was not easily swayed by enthusiastic sighs.

This time Sylvia did settle down. For two whole weeks she was on her own before they sent another girl. When the newcomer arrived, Sylvia was dismayed to see that it was a half-caste girl by the name of Anita, whom she had encountered at the remand home in Norwood. Anita had been the instigator of many fights in the past; she had also been the one to attack Sylvia with a coke bottle. But it was different here. Sylvia, as the first girl to arrive, commanded respect, had automatic seniority, and the two girls became friends.

★ ★ ★

Sylvia was at Kent for nearly two months and for the first time in ages she found herself actually liking her situation. Just when she had decided that all would now be well with her, Miss Wilson paid one of her regular dutiful visits.

"The department has decided that you must move on," she announced. "I'm sorry, dear, but if you hadn't kept on running away . . . "

"But I don't do it now, do I?"

I'm afraid it's come just a little too late. We think you should be put somewhere where you will not be able to abscond from. After all, you must understand, we have a duty to be responsible for you. You were placed in our care, after all."

Sylvia's heart sank. Would she ever find anywhere where she could be happy? Why didn't they just leave her alone? It wasn't fair to keep shifting her about all the time. All right, so she had run away, but nobody had taken the trouble to find out why she had. She tried to explain this to Miss Wilson, but came up against a barrier.

"I'm sorry, Sylvia. I've heard all your false promises before. We just can't afford to take another chance. Yes, I know you like it here, but how long will it be before you get the wanderlust again? No, I'm sorry, my mind is made up. Now get your things together and hurry; we have to drive to Surrey and it's getting late. I don't want to be snarled up in a traffic jam. I have another girl to see later."

Sylvia bade a despondent farewell to Anita.

"Where are you going? Why are you going?"

"I don't know!" Sylvia answered miserably.

"Chin up! I'll keep your place until you come back."

"I . . . I don't think I'm coming back."

"Of course you are. I'll have a word with my social

worker and see what he has got to say. I'm sure you'll be back in no time at all."

* * *

Another grey building loomed up at the end of a long driveway. The gates leading to it were locked and had to be opened by a porter, who inspected the documents provided by Miss Wilson, before deciding that it was all right to let them in.

Sylvia thought it looked like a hospital, and she was right. It was a hospital, but not an ordinary one. This was St Ebba's for the mentally ill, into which category Sylvia had unwittingly placed herself by her constant running away. She was to have some tests done to decide whether she was mentally deficient in some way, and to get to the root of the reason why she seemed unable to cope with her problems in the outside world.

They drove through the spacious grounds, passing the pointers to the various wards which, Sylvia noticed, were named after trees. The car stopped outside Holly Ward and Miss Wilson got out. Armed with her documents, she went to ring the bell.

A nurse came hurrying along the corridor, looking flustered. She had a bunch of keys on a long chain hanging from her pocket, and she selected the appropriate one. As the door opened before Sylvia, she heard a caterwauling that made her flesh crawl.

"Be quiet, Mrs. Shaw!" the nurse said sternly. Then more kindly to Sylvia: "Come along, Sylvia. I'll show you to your bed. Here's a locker where you can put some of your belongings. Have you any photo's of your family that you want to put on the top? You haven't? Well, never mind, dear, I'm sure someone will send some in. It makes it rather cosy, don't you think?"

Leaving the girl to unpack her clothes, the nurse returned to the doctor's office where Miss Wilson had gone to confer about Sylvia's case.

Sylvia glanced around the ward dubiously; some of the patients looked hostile. An old woman with white hair came by, suddenly spat at her and walked off. Another woman, seeing what had happened, came over and sat down on Sylvia's bed.

"You mustn't mind Mrs. Shaw, she gets like that sometimes. Senile you know, poor thing! Anyway, I'm Eileen, what's your name? And what are in for?"

Sylvia started to cry. She felt so alone. Once glance at all the barred windows and the locked doors, told her that this was a place from which she could not escape.

"I think it has something to do with running away from the homes that I've stayed in," she said finally.

Eileen thought it must be something more than that. She herself was in for stabbing a woman who had been sleeping with her husband. That nice young doctor had given her silly tests with pieces of paper and blobs of ink on them. She had to say what they reminded her of and she had said they looked like blobs of ink! The doctor had been impressed and, when Eileen left the room, she heard him tell the others that she was a psychopath. She didn't know what it meant, but it sounded grand. She was waiting to be moved to the secure unit at Elm Lodge, but she was not bothered as she had friends there who she had spoken to from the windows when she had been walking in the grounds.

Holly Ward was only an assessment block – something like a reception centre – where patients were held until they were seen by the doctor. Then, according to his findings, they were despatched to another part of the hospital. This was where Sylvia was to spend the next few days until her tests were carried out.

The kindly nurse came back and took her down to the day room, which also served as a dining room. A television set dominated one side of the room, while a small wireless was on a table to one side. At the end of the room were double wooden doors which led through into Ash Lodge, the men's reception centre. Sylvia wandered over to the wireless and turned it on. Strains of Danny Vee singing 'Take Good Care of My Baby' issued forth, and she began to sing along with the record. Mrs. Shaw, who had been sitting quietly in the corner, jumped to her feet, crossed the room and, without a word, switched the wireless off. She also took the opportunity to spit at Sylvia again.

"Now, Mrs. Shaw, sit down, there's a good girl," the nurse wheedled patiently. "I'm sorry," she went on, turning to Sylvia. "She's old and not aware of what she is doing. She doesn't mean any harm."

Sylvia eyed the old woman warily. So far she had not heard her speak and wondered whether she could do anything other than spit.

"Psst! I say, you in there. Come here!"

The voice seemed to be coming from out of the wall. Sylvia turned her head. Then she noticed that the double wooden doors behind her were slightly ajar and there was a face pressed up against the small opening.

"Come here!" The voice had become insistent. "Don't let them see you."

She decided that she would ignore it, so she remained where she was for a while.

"Come over here, please."

Sylvia made sure the nurse wasn't watching, before wandering over nonchalantly to the voice.

"What do you want?" she hissed.

"Just to talk. What's your name? How long have you been here?"

"My name is Sylvia and I've only just arrived."

Suddenly the door opened wider and she managed to get a good look at the person standing there. He was a short man, about five foot one, and aged about twenty-two. He looked harmless enough, quite pleasant in fact.

"Do you want to come to the pictures on Saturday?"

Sylvia laughed dryly. "I shouldn't think so! I'm locked in and can't get out."

"That's simple. I know all the ways out. Sometimes, if you're good, they let you have a pass for the afternoon; but you're new here, so I don't think you'll get one. Leave it to me, I'll sort something out. I'm called Nobby, by the way, Nobby Clark."

Sylvia thought that was a silly name for a man. She didn't realise that many people who are called Clark are nicknamed Nobby. She went back to sit down and found Mrs. Shaw staring at her from across the room. It was an uncomfortable situation, so after a time Sylvia decided to ask the old lady why she was staring. She kept her distance as she posed the question, in case she got spat at again; but now Mrs. Shaw only gazed blankly ahead.

Sylvia gave it up as a bad job and sat down to wait for the evening meal. With the exception of Eileen, nobody bothered to speak to her. The meal would have passed uneventfully had it not been for Mrs. Shaw, who tipped her plate of food all over the nurse's head. Sylvia watched in awe as the nurse calmly wiped herself down and carried on trying to feed the old lady again.

At bedtime, another nurse came round with pills for the ward. She paused by Sylvia's bed, studying her notes and then handed her two blue tablets from the trolley, with a glass of water to swallow them down. She explained that these would help her to sleep.

Sylvia took the proffered tablets without protest and popped them into her mouth. She slept soundly until morning when she was awoken with a cup of tea. She told the nurse that she didn't like tea and it was taken away and a cup of warm, milky coffee brought in its place.

After breakfast, she was told to report to the doctor's office to take some tests. The nurse took her down the corridor and tapped gently on the door.

"Come in!"

The nurse smiled at her reassuringly and ushered her inside.

The doctor was good-looking. Young, but mature; he looked a bit like Ricky Nelson, Sylvia decided.

"Sit down, please." He motioned to a chair the opposite side of his desk. "I'm Doctor Melia and I want you to look at these pictures and tell me what you see."

Sylvia thought the doctor had a nice voice with a slight soft accent which she couldn't quite define. She examined the set of six pictures and at first glance couldn't make out anything at all. Screwing up her eyes and peering more closely, she saw what looked like two vases. She told the doctor as much.

"Good!" he said. "Can you see any people in the picture? There! He indicated a shape between the two vases."

Sylvia could now that he had pointed them out. She completed the test very quickly, making out different figures and shapes every time she looked at them. The next test was to place blocks of wood in the various shapes provided. It reminded her of something one did in an infant school. She told the doctor that she thought it was too easy.

"Aah!" he said, tapping the end of his nose with a pencil. "It might look easy, but I can assure you that all these tests mean something."

Sylvia returned to her ward none the wiser; but later that day she was transferred to Larch Cottage. It was a relief to get away from Mrs. Shaw and her spitting. She did wonder if Nobby would take her to the pictures, as he had promised.

Larch Cottage was not as bright and airy as Holly Ward had been. There were many people here and the long line of beds filled the sleeping ward. A young girl caught Sylvia's attention. The girl was walking round and round a carpet, pausing occasionally to shout in a loud voice: "Teapot! Sausages! Teapot! Sausages!" On and on, all day long without variation or elaboration.

"Why does she do that?" Sylvia asked a woman standing nearby.

"No one knows really," replied the woman. "She's only fourteen, you know. Raped at the age of seven. It must have turned her brain. Poor Pamela!" The woman giggled maliciously and Sylvia felt afraid.

The woman told her that her name was Eva and that she had been a reporter in the Second World War. Later that evening, for no apparent reason, Eva suddenly turned on the nurses and began to fire an imaginary machine gun at them:

"Rat tat tat! Rat tat tat!"

Two nurses hurried out of the day room and grabbed her by the arms. Eva shouted and screamed, but they had quickly pinned her down. Two other nurses came and helped to carry her into the sleeping ward. There, on the bed, they lifted up her frock and administered a shot of paraldehyde which caused the unfortunate woman to fall asleep in seconds.

Sylvia was horrified. The truth suddenly dawned on her: she was in a mental hospital! She must be the only sane one here. When the nurses returned and this time grabbed Pamela, she sprang into action.

"Don't take her! Why pick on her? She's done nothing wrong."

They ignored her, pushing her roughly aside.

Sylvia incensed by their meanness, tried to protect the girl. She kicked out at the nurses and the next minute found herself being taken to a padded cell. She just had time to look at the rubber mattress on the floor and a single blanket thrown over it, before receiving a jab of paraldehyde herself.

"I won't go to sleep!" she cried. "I . . ." She was unconscious in seconds.

*   *   *

"Have you learnt your lesson yet?"

Sylvia pulled herself up groggily. Her mouth was dry and there was a funny smell about her. Her head was thumping and she felt sick. What was that smell? It was like nothing she had encountered before. It was not like her father's breath when he had come into her room at night. It smelt strong, like antiseptic. She rubbed her eyes and peered up at the nurse.

"I didn't do anything wrong . . ." she finally ventured.

"Attacking a nurse is hardly not doing anything wrong, now is it? You can come back to the ward if you promise to behave yourself."

All day long, Sylvia thought of ways and means to escape. The trouble was, she wasn't yet allowed out of the ward. When she next saw the doctor, she would ask him if she could have a pass to go into Epsom, which was only down the road.

Two weeks later, she was nowhere nearer to achieving her freedom. Miss Wilson was coming to visit today, and she had promised to take Sylvia out. Sylvia still had bad feelings towards her for inflicting this punishment on her, but she had finally resigned herself to accept the fact that to escape confinement, even for a brief while, was better than nothing at all . . .

She enjoyed her afternoon away from the hospital. She returned with two new frocks which had been bought for her by Miss Wilson, courtesy of the department. The other patients, some of whom had not seen the outside world in many years, hung anxiously onto her description of where she had been and what she had done.

"They're nice," said Eva, fingering the frocks. "You'd better put them away safely."

"Oh I will!" Sylvia assured her.

But they weren't safe enough. By evening they had both been ripped to shreds and placed on Sylvia's bed. Sylvia had no idea who could have been spiteful enough to do this. She reported it to the nurses, who merely said that it was up to her to take more care of her personal belongings. It was difficult in a place like this where no one could keep anything private. Sylvia never did find out who was responsible, but she made sure after that that anything else she had was well hidden.

Chapter Fifteen

Sylvia spent a little over ten months at St. Ebba's. During that time, apart from that fracas in the beginning with a nurse on Larch Cottage, she was a model patient. Her tests proved that she was way above average intelligence and the review board, sitting on her case, decided that she should be sent somewhere less confined.

They chose Belmont Hospital, where the patients had psychological problems rather than mental ones. One of the wings was dedicated to helping youngsters adapt to life on the outside. It was a new project run by the patients for the patients and included self-help therapy. Sylvia could do as she liked provided that she was prepared to take the consequences for her own actions, and talk about them afterwards.

Arrangements were made to send her there within the week. A letter was sent to Belmont to confirm that a place would be found for her on arrival. When the reply came, it was disappointing. The wing to which Sylvia was to have been assigned was full, and a place had been made for her in the actual hospital itself.

Belmont wasn't as frightening to Sylvia as St. Ebba's had been. The wards were smaller and the people seemed almost normal. The main bonus was that the regime was more relaxed, so that she was able to go into the nearby village of Sutton whenever she liked.

There was a music room set back in another part of the building which not many people used; here she could often be found curled up with a book in a large armchair, listening to the latest popular music. It was heaven compared to St. Ebba's! Regular dances were held where she met many new friends and had her fair share of attention from boys eager to partner her. Once a week films were shown. It was here that she first saw Pat Boone in 'April Love'. There were also classes in numerous subjects from cooking to basket making. None of these particularly appealed to her. She was not forced to attend, although many attempts were made to persuade her. Sylvia became wise to this and would hide down on the railway lines which ran at the bottom of the hospital.

There was a pub called 'The California', which was just over the other side of the railway. Many of the patients liked to go there to unwind, forget about their problems and make new friends. One Saturday evening, Sylvia was asked if she would like to go and have a drink with several of the other patients. The crossing place they were supposed to use was a foot-bridge a bit further down; but as it was out of the way, they ran across the lines instead, narrowly avoiding the oncoming trains that bore down on them out of the tunnel.

It was on this occasion that Sylvia met David, a Joe Brown lookalike, with blond hair cropped short and a boyish grin. He told Sylvia that he suffered from depression. Now that he had received treatment, he hoped to be leaving in a month or two's time. He bought her a pint of bitter which, at eleven pence, was one of the cheapest drinks. Sylvia felt very grown up as she sipped the bitter liquid. The drink went straight to her head, though, making her giggly and light-headed, and she made no objection when David put his arm around her as they crossed back over the railway lines.

David had his own room in the hospital, in the wing which had originally been earmarked for Sylvia. She made no protest as he led her to the bed and undressed her. The drink had made her totally relaxed. There, in that room, she made love for the first time. It felt nothing like what her father did to her when he told her he loved her. Then it had hurt. But now, David made love to her, so gently and so tenderly that she felt her heart would burst with happiness. The next morning he was obliged to attend a ward meeting to discuss his actions of the previous night. It made no difference to his feelings for Sylvia. From that day on they were inseparable. He accompanied her to the dances and bought her records out of the money he earned from working in a butcher's shop in the village.

★ ★ ★

The California soon became a part of lives, although sometimes David didn't accompany her as he still suffered from bad bouts of depression. Sylvia didn't know how to cope with him when he got into one of these moods, but found that it was best to ignore him when he was in this frame of mind. He would tell her to go to the pub without him which she was reluctant to do, despite having made many friends.

One day she and David decided to go into Belmont shopping. They popped into the Toast Rack, a local coffee bar, for some warm buttered toast and a cup of frothy coffee. David wandered over to the juke box and studied the selections. He placed his money in the slot and the strains of Gerry and the Pacemakers filled the room. An attractive girl sat at a nearside table singing along to the music. Every now and then the girl would glance over at David, catch his eye and then look quickly away again. Sylvia was enjoying her toast too much to notice the looks that passed between them. So when David said he was going outside for a breath of air, Sylvia said absentmindedly "Oh, all right then." and turned her attention back to the toast. She didn't even notice the girl get up to leave as well.

David began making excuses not to see Sylvia. He

had a headache. He was depressed. Sylvia let it go on. He was just in one of his moods she reasoned. But soon the days slipped into weeks and Sylvia became very concerned about him. Then a friend asked if she and David had quarrelled.

"Of course not." she replied smiling. "He's just having a bad time of it recently. I am a bit worried though because he should be leaving soon, and he's not shown any signs of getting better."

"Well," the friend continued, "I only asked because I saw him at the pictures last Saturday with another girl."

Sylvia frowned. "No, I think you must be mistaken."

"Oh no. It's no mistake. I definitely saw him with another girl." the friend persisted.

Sylvia left her unfinished drink on the bar, rushed across the railway lines, then over to the hospital wing and right up to the window of David's room. The curtains were shut. But then . . . she distinctly saw two shadows silhouetted against the curtains. She strained her ears to try and hear what was being said, but the noise from the trains muffled any conversation that they might be having. Then as she stood and watched like a peeping tom, she saw the two shadows entwine – the light went out and nothing . . .

Sylvia's heart was racing. What should she do? Confront him and probably cause a scene? Keep quiet and let the anger build up? In the end she decided to confront him. Marching round to the entrance, she flung open the doors and strode purposefully down the corridor that led to David's room. She banged on the door angrily. Then again and again until his voice could be heard inside to say, "Hang on a minute."

Suddenly the door opened and a dishevelled David stood before her, blinking his eyes at the light which shone into his room from the corridor.

"Sylvia. What are you doing here?" he stammered, guilt written all over his face. "I wasn't feeling very good and thought I'd get an early night. What are you doing?" he said as Sylvia pushed rudely past him and into the room. There under the candlewick bedspread lay a shape. Sylvia pulled the cover back and saw to her horror the girl she had only fleetingly glanced at in the Toast Rack. The girl grabbed ineffectively at the cover to try and hide her nakedness.

"You, you . . . How could you? I trusted you." Sylvia rounded angrily on David.

"I can explain."

"Oh yes, I bet you can. Get dressed. Now!" she screamed as she threw the girl's clothes at her.

"Calm down Sylvia." David touched her arm.

Sylvia backed away, palms towards him to fend him off. "Don't touch me . . . ever."

With that she turned and ran back to her ward, not even stopping to talk to her other friends who were just returning back from their night out at the California.

"What's got into her tonight?" One of them was heard to ask.

"I'm sure I don't know. But it looks as if she's got the wind up her tail." laughed another, as they continued on their way.

* * *

The next morning at breakfast, David tried approaching Sylvia but she turned her back away and totally ignored him. David persisted during the course of the next week to make attempts to talk to her. All to no avail. Sylvia was truly hurt and wouldn't let him get near her. She surrounded herself with friends in order not to have to speak to him. Finally on the Friday evening at the dance, David seized his opportunity. He saw Sylvia sitting on her own in a darkened corner watching the others dancing to a slow smoochy record. He went up behind her, pulled her to her feet and dragged her on the dance floor.

"Just what do you think you're doing?" she hissed.

"I've been trying to talk to you for over a week now and you won't listen, so now you'll have to." he told her.

David pulled her close breathing in the sweet smell of her body. "You don't know how much I've missed you." he groaned. "I've been a fool. Please forgive me."

"I can't." Her tears began to fall, slowly at first, then in floods, and the sound of her sobs filled the room.

"Come on. Come back to my room." When he saw that Sylvia made no protest, he led her by the arm off the dance floor and back to his room.

Sylvia sat on the edge of the bed. David sat on the bed beside her. He took her into his arms and gently rocked her. "Shh, my love. It's going to be all right."

Sylvia wept uncontrollably in the comfort of his arms. "We've been through such a lot together."

David held her tight. "I know." Her tears were wetting his shoulder. He lightly kissed her cheek, she raised her head and he held her tear-stained face in his hands. Suddenly his lips were on hers, softly at first, then with ardour and passion. She didn't pull away. At this moment she needed love and affection so very much.

He kissed her mouth, face and neck, all the while whispering how much he loved her. He gently pushed her back on to the pillow and, lying beside her, ran his hand down her neck. He calmly slipped the thin straps of her brassiere from her shoulders, and moved his hand slowly over her breasts. Nothing was hurried.

Sylvia caught her breath. She hadn't planned this. She knew it was wrong but she didn't stop him. He fondled and kissed her breasts, running his tongue over the taut nipples, very slowly and deliberately. Sylvia thought she was going to explode with desire. He was caring and loving, and all the while whispering tender words. Feelings were going through she had never felt before. Now David's hand was sliding over her petticoat. He pulled it above her waist and caressed her thighs. She wanted to scream out with pleasure. Then his warm hand was on her flat stomach. It wasn't demanding or rushed. She felt like dying in a sea of ecstasy.

"Sylvia, I want you so much," he murmured thickly.

She couldn't answer.

"May I?"

She wanted to cry out, "Please, please, please . . ."

Then suddenly the thought of the other woman filled her mind. She pushed David's hand away. "I'm sorry David. I shouldn't have let you go this far.

He grabbed her hand. "Please, Sylvia. Don't try and stop me, not now."

"No, David! We mustn't." She sat up and self-consciously straightened her clothes. "I can't."

He sat up and ran his hands through his cropped hair. "Why? I thought you loved me."

"I do like you. But I don't love you."

"You don't have to love . . . What if I go away and get killed?"

"David, don't say things like that. Don't try and blackmail me. It won't work." She reached over to the bedside table, picked up a packet of cigarettes and offered him one. "I'm very fond of you, and I like your company, but I can't help thinking about that other girl. You know I'd never do anything to hurt you like that."

"Good then aren't you," said David sarcastically. He stood up and lit his cigarette.

"Please don't be angry with me. I'm sorry, it's my fault, I shouldn't have let it get so far." Sylvia felt very guilty. Her thoughts were in a turmoil. "I think it best that I leave now."

David shrugged. "That's up to you."

As Sylvia went to leave the room, she turned to him and said once again, "Please don't be angry with me, I still want us to be friends. Maybe one day it will be something more when I have learnt to trust you again."

David made no move towards her, neither did he offer to walk her back. But when she had gone, he placed his head in his arms and wept.

*　*　*

The next day he didn't turn up for work. Nobody had seen him since late the previous evening. A search of the grounds was made and, tragically, David's body was found on the railway. It was not known whether he had been trying to cross the lines and had got caught by a train, or whether it was a suicide attempt. It was a secret that he took with him to his grave.

Sylvia retreated into her shell, rebuffing all attempts to try to talk to her about it. She was convinced that she was the cause behind David's suicide. She went down into the village and bought a bottle of hydrogen peroxide. In the bathroom at the hospital, she attacked her hair with a pair of scissors until it resembled a hedgehog. Then she tipped the whole bottle of peroxide over it and went to bed wearing a bath hat which she left on all night. In the morning, when she took the hat off, her hair had dried like straw and was a bright yellow. It made her face look pasty. Always before, she had cared lovingly for her black hair and had been proud of it, rinsing it with vinegar after the wash to make it shine. Now it looked dull and lifeless.

It was her act of bravado. The hospital became increasingly concerned about her and sent her to talk with the psychiatrist, Doctor Sampson. He sat for hours with her, patiently trying to prise things out of her about her past. By now, Sylvia was less amenable that she had been and these sessions normally ended with her storming out and swearing as she slammed the door behind her. Then she would come back into the room to see what effect, if any, this had had, and to apologise before banging the door again on her way out.

One night, she went missing. Torches lit up the grounds and voices called her name, getting no response. She had taken refuge in the bushes edging the railway line. She felt groggy, ill. She had gone to the village earlier that day and bought fifty aspirin and some orangeade. When darkness fell she crept out of the hospital and down to the railway line where she took the whole bottle of pills washed down with the orangeade.

She had no reason to live. Nobody knew where she was. Her family had gone. Her old school friends had all lost contact with her. She had no one except a crummy old social worker who came to see her when she felt like it. Dying seemed the easiest way out. She had nothing any more . . .

"Bring the torch over here, I think I've found her!"

She was vaguely aware that she was being lifted up and a blanket wrapped round her. In the hospital wing, where they had laid her, there were more lights and voices.

"What happened? Have you taken anything? Talk to me!"

Sylvia wanted to sleep. She didn't want to answer questions.

"Leave me alone! I'm tired! Let me die!"

"I think she's taken something. We ought to give her a stomach pump whether she has or she hasn't. Nurse, fetch the necessary equipment! Quickly now!"

A thin rubber tube was placed down one of Sylvia's nostrils and salt water was poured down it. It had the desired effect for, after a few coughs, she was violently sick.

"There now," a voice soothed. "You'll soon feel better. You're a very silly girl, aren't you, Sylvia? Why did you do it?"

Tears coursed down the girl's cheeks. They ought to have left her alone! Just a few more minutes and it would all have been over.

She spent a day in the hospital wing before being allowed back into the ward with the others; there she would sit for hours without speaking. Her stomach was sore and tender to the touch and her nose took some time to heal having been bruised by the struggle to insert the tube. The nurses kept a watchful eye on her, although they could not be vigilant twenty-four hours a day. Time slowly passed and the unfortunate episode was not repeated.

* * *

Gradually Sylvia made progress. She had met Ian, who helped her to get over the worst of it. Ian was uncannily like Elvis Presley: he could sing like Elvis and wore his hair like him. Sylvia loved to sit and listen to him serenading her.

He was a nice enough lad, but he wasn't David. Sylvia still missed him terribly, but she was sensible enough to realise that she couldn't grieve forever. Her black moods became less frequent and she began to settle down. Ian taught her how to roll cigarettes, or at least the principle of the thing. She would end up laughing when she rolled one so big that the tobacco fell out of the end, then one so tight and small that it would go out as soon as you lit it. Finally, he bought her a cigarette rolling machine, and after a time she could roll one almost as well as he could. Unfortunately the relationship with Ian came to an abrupt end when he was discharged. She had never found out how he came to be in Belmont in the first place. Ian kept matters close to his heart and found it hard to confide in anyone, even Sylvia, whom he had grown very attached to. But Sylvia couldn't dwell on his departure for too long as she had matters to contend with herself. Little did she realise that their paths were to cross again one day in the future.

Chapter Sixteen

It was January 1963, and Sylvia had just turned nineteen. The hospital board met and it was decided that,
after more than a year at Belmont, she was in danger
of becoming institutionalised: a job on the outside
would help to ease her back towards a normal life. A
place was accordingly found for her in a laundry
works nearby. Although the management knew she
was an in-patient at the hospital, the staff were not
informed.

At first Sylvia enjoyed her new found freedom. The
salary certainly seemed more attractive than the paltry
pocket money handed to her each week by the hospital. She had new friends and everything went
smoothly until one day when she mentioned that she

was staying in Belmont. Attitudes then began to change, and friendships to wither.

The works manager was distressed and asked her why she had thought fit to tell them about her illness. Sylvia hadn't until now thought of herself as ill; but she told him that she had no wish to lie to anyone. The cold-shouldering of her by the staff left her with no option but to leave.

The hospital staff told her that if they were lucky enough to find her another job, she should not tell anyone of her background. Sylvia reluctantly agreed to this, and so found herself in a baker's shop in Rosehill, a bus ride away. This was more like it, she thought to herself. She liked meeting the customers and passing the time of day with them. The wages were good – more than she had earned at the laundry – and she was punctual. Her attitude to life became more outgoing and her personality blossomed.

The next stage came quickly. The hospital authorities felt that the time had come when she could be discharged. Welfare found her a place in a girls' hostel in Chelsea and a job at a garage in Victoria doing general office work.

From the start, Sylvia didn't like the hostel. She was sharing a room with three other girls who came and went all hours of the night. Sylvia liked to go to bed early, but she got little benefit from it, as she would be constantly disturbed in the early hours of the morning. Her job was boring and repetitive; the only redeeming factor was the generous salary that accompanied it, and Tony, the apprentice mechanic.

"Hello gal. Gonna put the kettle on?

"Oh Tony, if you drink any more tea you'll have it coming out of your earholes." Sylvia laughed. She went and filled the kettle with water. Then she busied herself washing up the cups. "Look at the state of this?" she groaned. "It's got greasy fingerprints all over it."

Tony came over wiping his hands on his overalls. "Sorry Syl, but I can't stop my hands from getting mucky, can I?"

Sylvia looked him up and down. "Nor on the rest of you by the looks of it. What do you do, bath in the stuff?" She licked her finger and then began vigorously scrubbing at a dirty mark just above his eye.

Tony caught hold of her hand. "Tell me what you really think of me. Do you think I'm a grease monkey and can't look decent?"

Sylvia pulled away quickly. "I didn't say that."

"I know you didn't say it, but it's what you're thinking, isn't it? Look, I'll tell you what, come out with me on Saturday night and I'll show you what I really look like out of these overalls.

Sylvia hesitated.

"What's wrong with you? You never talk about yourself, whether you have a boyfriend . . ." Tony looked at her waiting for her reply.

"No, I don't have a boyfriend and no I don't want to talk about myself. There is nothing about me that you would find very interesting." she smiled ruefully.

"Aw cmon Syl, give me a chance . . . please." Tony begged. "Just come out with me once, then if you don't like me . . . well fair enough, I won't ask you again."

"All right then, but let me make it clear that I am not ready for a boyfriend just yet. So long as you understand that I am going out with you as a friend . . . nothing more."

"Thanks Syl. You won't regret it, I promise." Tony's face lit up.

Sylvia began to regret that she had agreed to go out with him. Friend or not. After David, she found it hard to make relationships. David had hurt her badly and the scars from his suicide were still raw in her memory. She didn't want to let the same thing happen again. But, if she thought about it logically, she was being very silly allowing herself to retreat from what others could offer her. She couldn't wrap herself up in cotton wool forever.

★   ★   ★

On Friday evening just before she left work, Tony came hurrying over to her. "How do you fancy coming to a party with me tomorrow?"

"Oh, but I thought we were going to the pictures."

"Well we still can if you want, but it's my birthday and my folks are throwing a party for me. I can hardly not turn up . . . can I, seeing as it's in my honour? It's my twenty first so I suppose they feel obliged to make something of it."

"Tony. Why didn't you let me know sooner?" Sylvia asked. "I haven't even got you a present."

"I didn't think you would agree to go out with me if I told you the truth." Tony replied honestly.

"I haven't been to a party in years, so yes, it could be fun." Sylvia didn't dare tell him the truth which was, she had never been to a party in her life. "Where shall I meet you?"

"Can you get to Victoria Station by seven o'clock?"

"Yes, but whereabouts?"

"I'll meet you under the clock then, at that time."

Sylvia giggled.

"What's so funny?" Tony sounded hurt.

"I wasn't laughing at you, silly. I was thinking about an old film that I once saw starring Robert Taylor and Vivian Leigh. I think it was called Waterloo Station. It was a real weepie and I cried buckets. He fell in love with this dancer and then because it was wartime, he kept being sent away. Everytime he went away they had an agreement that they would always meet up under the clock at the station. One day, she wasn't there . . ."

"Yes, go on." Tony urged.

"I can't finish it." Sylvia's eyes started to fill with tears. It was too close to home when she remembered that Vivian Leigh had thrown herself under a bus at Waterloo Bridge. Robert Taylor had gone back looking for her over many years. One day he finally discovered the truth what had happened to his sweetheart.

"Sorry." Tony could see she was distressed.

Pulling herself together, Sylvia confirmed that she would see him at Victoria Station tomorrow.

* * *

Saturday morning was hectic. Sylvia rushed out to buy herself something new to wear to the party. As luck would have it there was a sale on in Bazaar, a boutique in the Kings Road which had been opened up by Mary Quant in 1955. Mary Quant was definately the 'in' place for fashion although her prices reflected her fame. This time however, Sylvia was in luck when she saw a gorgeous mini skirt and top just made for her. And, at a price she could afford. Armed with her purchases she set off in search for a new pair of shoes. Further on down the road she spotted a pair of long white PVC boots which she thought would compliment her new outfit admirably. Next on the agenda was to buy something for Tony. She had no idea what he wore outside of work, but thought it would probably be something trendy. Passing a new man's clothing shop that had sprung up, she was intrigued to see a lovely paisley shirt in the window. She decided that it would suit Tony very well and went inside.

"Oh yes madam, it's from our very new and exciting range," the rather effeminate shop assistant assured her. "but if it doesn't suit, you can come back and change it."

Sylvia liked it better now that she had examined it. It was high-necked with a button down collar.

"Thank you. I'll take it." she said.

"Would madam like it gift wrapped?"

"How much extra will that be?" she asked.

"Absolutely nothing. It's all part of our service." the assistant beamed at her.

Sylvia watched while he carefully wrapped it. His movements were exaggerated as he reached under the counter, found a length of pretty ribbon and deftly tied it round the parcel into a neat bow.

He handed it over with a smile. "There we are then. I hope he likes it. He's a lucky man to have such a nice present."

The rest of her day was spent experimenting with make-up. She didn't wear much, only a slight touch of green eyeshadow to accentuate her eyes. That morning, swept away with the excitement of the party, she had treated herself to some Miners blue eyeshadow, Rimmel liquid eyeliner, Max Factor black mascara and a tube of Pan Stick. Now she stood in front of the mirror trying it on. She decided against the Dusty Springfield look. It made her look like a ghost with all that pan-stick on her face and eyes thick with black mascara. It made matters worse when one of her room mates popped back because she'd forgotten her handbag and laughed her head off at the sight that Sylvia presented. When she had gone, Sylvia rubbed it all off until her face was red. She then tried the blue eyeliner, which in turn, made her look as if she had a black eye. Next she tried the pale pink lipstick, which ended up more on her teeth than on her lips.

"Sod it!" she said uncharacteristically, scooping the lot into a make-up bag where it would probably stay unused forever. "What a waste of money that was!"

And then went back and opted for her usual look with the green eyeshadow.

★ ★ ★

Tony had arrived before her and hurried over to her as she turned into the entrance hall. He let out a low wolf whistle. "What a pair of legs! What a figure? You look stunning!"

Sylvia felt pleased at his flattery and was glad that she had taken the time to buy something decent.

"Thanks." she said. "You don't look too bad your-self." It was the first time she had seen without his overalls on and he really did look smart, although not overdressed. He had on, a white polo necked sweater, ice cool blue jeans and black cuban heeled boots.

"Here, this is for you," she handed him the gift wrapped parcel shaking her head when he attempted to open it. "Not now, later."

They went outside and boarded the bus that would take them to Fulham. They alighted where Lillie Road joins Fulham Palace Road, walked a couple of hundred yards and turned the corner into Purcell Crescent. It was only a small road but Sylvia could see immediately which house was Tony's. Balloons and streamers festooned the front garden, and the sound of Beatle music could be heard emanating from the front room which had all the windows open.

"Well here we are then." Tony took Sylvia's hand and led her into the house.

A little girl of about seven suddenly hurled herself into Tony's arms.

"Happy birfday Tone."

Tony smiled fondly at her. "Thank you Joanie." he said, pulling playfully at her pigtails.

"Who's she?" asked Joanie, popping her thumb in her mouth and gazing shyly at Sylvia.

"Meet Sylvia, my friend from work."

Sylvia took the little girl's hand and solemnly shook it. "Hello Joanie," she said, smiling at the girl.

"She's nice." declared Joanie to her brother. "Are you his girlfriend?" she asked, addressing Sylvia.

Sylvia replied, "No, I'm just a friend."

"Put me down Tone." said Joanie. "Do you get dirty like my bruvver?"

Sylvia laughed and told Joanie that she didn't mess about with cars, just kept the office tidy.

Joanie, satisfied with this reply, ran off to join her friends.

"She's lovely, your sister. I like her."

"She likes you too. Come and meet Mum and Dad, then you will have met the whole family."

Sylvia got on well with Tony's parents. His dad, who worked as a brickie, was down to earth.

"Call me Bert." he told her, when they were introduced. Holding out his hand, he caught hers and shook it vigorously. "I'm sorry you've caught me unawares," he said, as he noticed her looking at his bare stomach which was poking out between his braces. I haven't had time to get washed, changed or put a clean shirt on yet. Ann, my wife, insisted that I get everything ready before I get all dolled up. Ah, talk of the devil, here she comes now."

Ann kissed Sylvia warmly. "You're a bit of a dark horse aren't you Tony? Fancy keeping her all to yourself."

Sylvia blushed, then started to explain that they were only friends.

"Oh well, perhaps it might lead to something more." muttered his Mother.

"What was that mum?" asked Tony.

"Nothing dear. I was only talking to myself. Come along Sylvia, I'm sure you would like something to eat."

The party went on until quite late. Sylvia looked at her watch and was horrified to discover that it was almost eleven thirty.

"Goodness me, I'll have to rush if I want to catch the bus home." she told Tony.

"There's really no need. You can always stay here in Joanie's room. She won't mind. I'm sure she'd love to wake up and see you in her bed."

"That's very kind of you, but I think I ought to be getting back."

Tony walked with her to the bus stop. They were just in time to catch the bus which was coming round the corner.

"Thanks for coming." Tony said, bending down to kiss her on the cheek. "I'll see you at work on Monday. Are you sure you'll be all right walking home so late at night? You're more than welcome to stay."

"Don't worry. I'll be fine. Thanks for inviting me. I really enjoyed myself. Bye."

She managed to get a cab from Victoria to Chelsea as she didn't fancy walking alone at night. When she arrived back at the hostel, she noted with some concern that the other's weren't back. As she got undressed for bed she hoped that they wouldn't come home drunk and wake her up again. She fell asleep with a smile playing on her lips reminiscing about Tony and his party. She didn't hear the others come in much later, she was far too busy dreaming.

* * *

Tony had been delighted with his shirt. It was just what he would have bought for himself. He told Sylvia so at work on the following Monday.

"I'm glad you liked it."

"How about coming out with me again, then you can see what it looks like on."

Sylvia, to her surprise, found herself agreeing.

He was very romantic and loved to surprise Sylvia. One weekend he took her to Cornwall.

"You're lucky," he said.

"Me?" asked Sylvia.

You're on holiday in Cornwall. And to top it all, you're here with me." He reached out and stroked her arm with the back of a sandy finger.

Sylvia laughed. "Big head," she cried, running off down the beach. He ran after her, took her hand and led her along the beach. They paddled in the surf, which glistened in the moonlight. And then he ran ahead and drew in the soft wet sand. It was her name and his, linked with a heart. Then he took her to a restaurant which was down a tiny alleyway. A stray evening breeze rippled the surface of the wine he had just poured. The food was excellent, so was the wine. Tony was fun, entertaining and charming.

"We are meant to be together," he said, pulling her towards him. And then he kissed her.

Finally she pulled away.

"It's getting late, we ought to be getting back."

"We needn't," he said. "Stay here with me."

"No . . ." she said. "This is happening too fast. I need time to think."

He let go of her hand, and followed Sylvia back to the hotel. This was their last night and Tony had hoped to make it special for her. Now it seemed to have gone wrong.

Sylvia lay awake, she couldn't sleep. Everytime she closed her eyes, she could see Tony's face. Were they really destined for each other?

The next morning they met at breakfast. Sylvia hardly touched a thing. They began the drive back to London in silence. Tony tried asking her if he had done something to offend her, but Sylvia reassured him that it was her fault and nothing that he had done.

They continued to go out together, but Tony sensed that since that weekend in Cornwall, their relationship was going backwards rather than forwards. It came as no surprise to him when one day Sylvia took him aside and told him that it was over.

"It's not because I don't like you, I do."

"Then why are you finishing it?"

"I just don't want to get too involved yet. I feel that you and your parents expect us to be a couple, get married . . . I'm not ready for that. I want to have fun while I'm still young enough to enjoy it." Seeing the hurt look on Tony's face, she felt sorry that she had allowed things to go this far. He had been the perfect gentleman, never pushing or pressurising her into doing anything she didn't want. A few kisses here and there, nothing more, and yet she felt claustrophobic. "I just need some time alone . . ."

Seeing Tony's woebegone face at work every day was too much for her. She knew she had hurt him, that he had expected more. But she had told him from the beginning that she only wanted his friendship. In the end she had little alternative but to leave. She told Tony of her decision.

"I wish you wouldn't Syl. You don't have to leave on my account you know."

"But don't you see, I can't face coming in here day after day seeing how miserable you look. You hardly talk to me any more. I can't bear this silence which goes on between us. Mr Huish has called me in the office several times recently to ask what is going on between us. He's told me he doesn't like having an atmosphere in his work place."

"I'll change then. I'll talk to you as normal. Just be your friend. Only please don't leave." Tony babbled.

"My mind's made up," she told him firmly. "I'm bored with the job and now I think it's time to move on. Besides," she continued, "I don't think I can stand living at the hostel for one minute longer. I hardly ever get a good nights sleep with all the comings and goings. I'm going to try and get my own place.

"It won't be easy you know. Accommodation is hard to find in London. Just give it another go."

Sylvia sighed. "No Tony, I've decided to make plans for myself for a change." She hated herself for hurting him like this, but it would be for the best in the end. She had thought it over very carefully, weighing up all the pro's and cons. For years she had been told what to do or what not to do. Jobs had been found for her, along with accommodation. Now she wanted to strike out on her own, to stand on her own two feet.

Wisely she found another job before handing in her notice; and it took only a few hours to fix herself up with a bedsit in Bayswater. She had chosen this area because the underground station at Queensway would drop her practically outside her new place of work. There wouldn't be much left from her salary of eight pounds and fifteen shillings by the time she had paid her rent of five guineas, but at least she would have the satisfaction of the privacy of her own room.

Excited at this prospect, she packed her few belongings and made arrangements to move in the next day. Fortunately for her, the landlord had not required the usual month's rent in advance. He seemed nice, although strict. He was Polish, and told her that she could not have visitors in her room after ten at night. She was to see to her own cleaning, but fresh sheets would be left at the beginning of the week. She felt happy to comply with these rules. After all, who did she know who would visit her anyway?

The following day found her in her new room on the second floor of a large house in Leinster Gardens. She unpacked her possessions and began to put them away. The room wasn't large, but it was adequate enough for her means. At least it was bright and had been freshly painted. She had been horrified at how much accommodation cost in London. Nearly every room she had seen had been over five pounds. Some were really grotty and not worth the money. She shuddered at the thought of some of them. Dirty walls, greasy patches on the bare carpet. No, this was decidedly luxurious compared to others. She pulled back the bottom sheet and was delighted to see a new mattress had placed on the bed. Her thoughts went back to a room she had seen in Holland Park. It was an attic room and she had been highly tempted by it. It had a lovely outlook over the park and nearby cricket field.

"It's a long way up." the landlady said, puffing her way to the top of the house. "Best room there is around here for miles and reasonable too."

Sylvia thought it debatable as it was more money than she had budgeted for.

"A real bargain at three pounds and seventeen shillings," the landlady went on. "My last tenant loved it so much, he would have stayed forever if he hadn't had to go abroad. Here we are then," she said, swinging open the door with a flourish. "You're only young so I don't think you'll find the stairs too much trouble. Take your time and have a look round. When you've finished come and tell me what you think."

On the surface, it looked a lovely room. Large,

bright and airy. A cooker stood in one corner, a sink in the other. Dominating the room was a big double bed in the centre. Sylvia sank down onto the bed. Then she frowned, it felt lumpy. She pulled back the cover and gasped with horror. The mattress was stained and dirty. She couldn't possibly think of sleeping on that! Next she inspected the cooker. The inside was covered with a thick layer of grease. The sink was next. This too was dirty and cracked. She ran the tap, brown water trickled slowly from it and lay in the bottom of sink. Sylvia wiggled her fingers down the drain in an attempt to try to dislodge whatever was keeping the water from draining away. When she pulled her fingers back she found they were covered with slimy loose hairs. She shuddered. She didn't want this room. It made her feel positively sick. She raced down the stairs and out of the front door without even telling the landlady that she didn't think she would take the room.

Finally with her things put away, Sylvia felt very much at home. Now at last she felt she was on her way to a new start in life. She was still young; perhaps one day, she would be able to forget the horrors of her earlier years. She had to make it work! She must make it work! She would make it work!

Chapter Seventeen

Sylvia enjoyed her new job in the toy department of a big store in Oxford Street. She had one regret, however, which was lack of funds. It was a struggle to make ends meet on three pounds and ten shillings, which was all she had left after paying her rent and her fares to work. She found herself living on bowls of tomato soup and bread until she was sick of the sight of the red liquid. She had thought of changing jobs and earning more money elsewhere, but it wasn't as easy as she had expected.

It was coming up to Christmas 1963 and she had been asked if she would work later on Thursday evenings each week to help replenish the stock in the toy department. It meant a little extra money for her, so she happily agreed. She would get off the tube at half past eight in the evening and take the short walk down Bayswater to Leinster Gardens where she lived, pausing on the way to gaze in the brightly lit windows of Whiteleys in Queensway.

It was on an evening such as this that she was approached by a smartly dressed elderly gentleman, who sidled up to her and whispered:

"Are you doing business?"

"I beg your pardon?"

"I said: 'Are you doing business?'" the man repeated.

Sylvia wondered what on earth he was talking about. She replied that she had just finished work and was on her way home.

The man laughed and explained patiently what the term 'business' meant.

Sylvia felt herself blushing at her own stupidity. She had heard of girls who went with men for money, but it had never occurred to her as something she was likely to do. She had never been approached before and didn't honestly think she was attractive enough for any man to want to pay for sexual services.

The man told her that his name was Alan and that he was in London to see some new clients in connection with his work. He was lonely and needed some female company. He said that she looked lonely, too, and that was why he had made his proposition.

"Look, I tell you what," he went on. "Why don't we go and have a bite to eat, have a little chat and then go back to your place? It'll be worth three pounds to you".

Sylvia hesitated. Then she thought about her stomach and how it could do with a good meal inside it, and how useful three pounds could be at the present time.

"All right, it's a deal," she said finally.

Alan took her to the Kardomah in Queensway, where she had her first taste of curry. The meal was delicious and so was the sparkling wine. She had two glasses of it and began to feel nice and relaxed and warm inside.

It had turned eleven when they left the restaurant and Sylvia began to have second thoughts about taking Alan back to her room. After all, it had been made clear to her that she was not allowed visitors after ten at night. So she told him that she would not be able to take him back with her because of the landlord and his rules.

"That's all right." he said. "Rules are made to be broken, you know. Anyway, if we creep in quietly, I don't suppose he'll even notice."

"I'm not so sure," she replied hesitantly. "All right then, but you'll have to be quiet."

Sylvia let herself in with her key and peered round the hallway. All was still; just a glimmer of light shone from under the landlord's door. She motioned to Alan and pointed towards the stairs. Shutting the door quietly behind them, she went ahead of him, her heart pounding. On the second floor landing she stopped and took another key out to open the door that led to her room. They went inside: they had done it! That was the first hurdle over with. Later she would have to get him out without being seen.

"Come here, you lovely girl." Alan patted his lap.

She went obediently and sat on his lap.

"Now tell me what you want me to do to you."

Sylvia felt embarrassed. She had no idea what was expected of her. The wine had still not lost its effect and gradually she relaxed.

Alan slid his hands up her jumper and started to play with her breasts. She found the sensation pleasing and began to respond. She felt that she was loved and wanted; all her life she had been crying out for affection. Very gently, Alan removed all her clothes until she stood there naked. She tried ineffectively to cover her body with her hands.

"No! Don't do that! Don't be ashamed, Sylvia. You have a lovely firm young body. You are quite beautiful."

He then undressed and stood before her, his manhood erect.

Sylvia glanced at him. She was not so sure that it was such a good idea after all. He was a lot older than her . . . old enough to be her father in fact. His body was a turn off. A big flabby stomach covered in spots which reached the point of his erection and around his buttocks. She began to wonder just what she had let herself in for. He might have some disease. Yes, she hadn't thought of that. Well, he looked all right with his clothes on, but now . . .

"I'm truly sorry, I've changed my mind. I don't think I can go through with this after all." Sylvia apologised.

"What do you mean? Oh I see, it's your first time isn't it? Don't worry, I'll be gentle with you. I'm not one of these kinky men you know."

Sylvia gritted her teeth as he lay beside her on the bed and started fumbling with his penis. Twice he tried to penetrate her and failed.

"Must have had too much to drink." he laughed.

Finally he managed to sustain his erection long enough for him to place it inside her. He pumped up and down for only a few moments before he exploded. Sylvia was aching with the weight of his body on top of hers. He tried to kiss her, but she turned her head away, reasoning that if she didn't allow him to do that, then it wouldn't mean anything to her. But it did. She felt dirty. She couldn't wait for him to leave so that she could have a bath and feel clean again.

"There, that was nice, wasn't it?"

Sylvia didn't answer.

"Was it nice for you?"

Still she didn't answer.

He stood up to put his clothes on and reaching into his wallet, he took out four pound notes.

"Thank you for a lovely evening," he said. "I did enjoy myself, and here is a little extra by way of thank you. I don't come to London very often, but when I do I hope to come and see you again. You have made a lonely man very happy."

Sylvia looked down at her feet. She didn't know what to say to him. He had been kind, but she wished she hadn't done it. Perhaps if she hadn't had wine with her dinner, then she would have had a clear head and this mightn't have happened. She would stay off the drink from now on she silently vowed.

"You'll have to be very quiet when you go out. I don't want the landlord to know that you've been here."

"I will be, never fear. Discretion is my middle name," he chuckled, winking at her in a knowing way.

She unlocked the door and started along the small corridor. The silence was broken only by a gentle snoring from behind one of the doors. She began to descend the stairs, grimacing when one made a creaking noise. Alan followed on tiptoe. They had just reached the hallway when the landlord's door was flung open and they were bathed in light.

"I varned you about visitors after ten, didn't I? Vat is the meaning of zis? I am haffing sleeping and hear a noise. I come out and see you vis zis man."

"I can explain," faltered Sylvia, trying desperately to rack her brains to think of something.

"I do not vish you to explain. Save your explanations for the morning when you can pack your things and get out of my house."

Alan went sneaking off and Sylvia was left to the landlord's wrath.

With his angry voice still ringing in her ears, she climbed the stairs wearily and collapsed on the bed. What on earth was she going to do now?

Morning came all too soon and with it the threatened eviction. The landlord was unrelenting. He did say, however, that she could leave her things here until she found a place. She begged him to wait until

Sunday, as she was working, and would have no time to look for another room until then. The answer was an emphatic No! He wanted her out now!

There was nothing more Sylvia could do to placate him. She rang up her work and told them that she was ill. They didn't seem too pleased about that. Then she counted up her wages to see if she had enough to get another place. It wasn't much . . . but then she remembered the four pounds that Alan had given her last night. It might be just enough to find something, but then again . . . what? She hadn't seen anything decent under five pounds when she first started looking for a room. She walked round all the local newsagents, looking at the advertisements for accommodation. When she spotted a few that sounded promising, she went to check them out, only to be told that they had already been let. Her feet were aching, as though she had walked all over West London. She went and sat down at the Wimpy bar in Queensway, misery etched all over her face. She ordered a cheese burger and started to eat it half heartedly.

"Do you mind it I sit here?" A man's voice interrupted her thoughts. "The other tables seem to be taken."

Sylvia didn't care where he sat so long as he didn't talk to her! She was unlucky. The man gabbled on but she hardly heard what he was saying, she was so wrapped up in her own thoughts.

"I said you look fed up. Want to talk about it?"

"Sorry, what did you say?" She looked at the man.

He wasn't as old as Alan but probably in his late thirties. He too was quite smartly dressed.

"I said, you look fed up. Do you want to talk about it? Maybe I can help."

"I shouldn't think so," Sylvia replied, but somehow found herself telling him a little of her predicament omitting to tell him the full reason as to why she was being thrown out of her bedsit. He looked kind enough, but then so did Alan and look where that had got her!

"You can come back to my place if you need somewhere to sleep for a few nights if you want." he said kindly.

Sylvia decided that at least that would be better than living rough. "All right then," she told him, "but I don't want to sleep with you. I'll only come if you promise that you won't touch me."

"What do you take me for? I'm only trying to help you. By the way, my name's Jack. What's yours?"

Sylvia told him as they walked down past Whiteleys, crossed the road and turned into St. Stephen's Gardens.

Sylvia immediately saw the double bed. "I don't think I can . . ." she faltered.

"It's all right, I promised I wouldn't touch you, didn't I?"

The first night passed without a hitch. The second night Jack tried to climb into her bed with her. On the third night Sylvia made a decision. She would leave first thing tomorrow.

When Jack got up in the morning to go to the toilet

which was further down the landing, Sylvia jumped up from the bed. She rushed to get dressed and started to go out of the front door. Suddenly she spotted his wallet laying on the top of his trousers. Stealthily she opened it and saw a wad of notes. She extracted a five pound note before replacing the wallet where she had found it. Then she crept to the front door, opened it and closed it gently behind her. She ran up Queensway not stopping until she had reached Hyde Park. What on earth was she doing? First a prostitute, now a thief! She sat down tiredly on a bench in Hyde Park. What a dilemma!

★ ★ ★

"Hullo, there, Remember me? It is Sylvia, isn't it?"

Sylvia brought her head up sharply to look at the speaker. At first she didn't recognise her. Then . . . recognition dawning, "Anita!" she yelled, "God, am I glad to see you! How did you know it was me? I can't have changed much since we last met. I really am pleased to see you, you know."

The half-caste girl smiled and sat down on the bench beside her. "It was your teeth that gave you away. I've never met anyone yet with teeth as big as yours."

"Thanks a lot." Sylvia said. She felt offended and hurt by the other girl's remark.

"Sorry. I'm only joking. At least they're nice and clean. Suppose they have to be considering they're on show all the time." Anita threw back her head and laughed. Then noticing that Sylvia looked tired, she asked concernedly, "What is it? You look all in. Are you ill or something?"

Sylvia found herself telling her all that had happened to her since she had left the home in St. Paul's Cray.

"I really thought you would come back, you know," Anita told her. "Crumbs, I didn't know you would end up in a looney bin. Mind you, I did have my doubts about you." She punched her friend playfully on the arm. Tell you what, let's go and have a cup of coffee."

They went to the Golden Egg at Marble Arch and Anita ordered two cups of coffee and a beefburger each. While Sylvia was biting hungrily into hers, she had a chance to study Anita. Gone was the wild tearaway girl that she once knew. In her place was a sophisticated-looking young woman, neatly dressed in the most fashionable clothes.

"Have you got a good job?" she enquired.

"Dear me, yes! An excellent job."

"Do you think they've got any vacancies?"

"Well, I don't know about that. Still, I suppose if you're not fussy about what you do . . ."

"Oh no!" Sylvia replied hastily.

"Are you living near here?"

"Well, I was, until the landlord threw me out a few days ago."

"What did he throw you out for?"

So Sylvia explained about that, too. When she had finished, Anita said that she could stay with her until she found a place of her own.

They went back to Leinster Gardens to pick up Sylvia's belongings which they loaded into a taxi. Anita gave the driver instructions to go to Lansdowne Way near Notting Hill Gate.

Anita had a spacious garden flat, which Sylvia looked around at in envy. Her friend must indeed earn an awful lot to afford a place like this, she thought. Accommodation in central London did not come cheap.

"You can put your clothes in here." Anita indicated the wardrobe, of which she had generously given up half. "The bathroom is through there if you want to freshen up."

Sylvia put her two best frocks in the wardrobe. They didn't take up much space! Whilst she was sorting out her few belongings, she marvelled at all the clothes her friend had. Most of them were showy evening frocks in a satin material. And the range of shoes! Why, she only had two pairs and they had both got holes in them.

Anita came back into the bedroom. "Is this all you have?" she asked incredulously.

"Fraid so."

"Never mind. I'll soon sort you out. For what I've got in mind, you'll need some decent clothes."

Sylvia ran a hot bath and put in a generous helping of foaming bath oil. She lay in the water for a long time, feeling lazy and luxurious; her anxieties about the immediate future pleasantly receded . . .

"I was wondering if this would fit you," said Anita, coming in with a slinky little black frock.

It was the most gorgeous dress that Sylvia had ever seen. It was soft to the touch and so flimsy. She was almost too scared to try it on in case she damaged it.

Sylvia looked at it incredulously. "I don't think it will cover much of me," she said, holding it up against her.

"Go on! Try it on!"

Sylvia drew up the zip and examined her reflection in the mirror. The frock certainly made her look more grown up, glamorous in fact. It fitted tightly in all the right places. It was cut low, emphasising her bust, and had a long split up the back. She slipped on a pair of slingback shoes with three inch heels, while Anita eyed her appraisingly.

"Yes," she said finally, "you look absolutely wonderful! Oh, you'll definitely do!"

"Will you tell me now what all the mystery is about?" asked Sylvia.

"Oh, it's no mystery, I can assure you. Look, sit down and I'll tell you all about it."

Anita began to explain how, when she had left the home in Kent, she had found a job; but how, like Sylvia, she had found that her money didn't go very far when she had to pay fares and rent. One day, in Soho, she had bumped into a man who told her that she had wonderful bone structure and should become a model. He then gave her his card and asked her to call him at his studio if she wanted to further her career. One day she decided to give him a ring. He invited her to the studio, and, after plying her with drinks laced with a drug, he proceeded to take pornographic pictures of her. She finally came to her senses and demanded to know what he had done. He laughed in her face and told her she was a common whore. She had cried when he said that she would never make a model, but would be better off selling her assets as a prostitute. She had a good body, which plenty of men would be willing to pay for, he said. Then he threw her out. No money, no modelling career. Standing in a doorway in Wardour Street shortly after the incident, she was surprised when a man approached her and asked if she was looking for him. She said she didn't even know who he was.

The man gave a throaty chuckle. "Everyone round here knows me," he told her. "I'm Frankie and this is the doorway to my club that you've chosen to stand in."

She said that she was sorry, she hadn't realised; she would move out of his way.

"Hey!" he replied. "Not so fast! I'd like to talk to you a bit more. How would you like a job working for me? Plenty of money. No problems. I could do with a good looker like you."

He told her that the job he was offering was as a hostess. Lots of bored and lonely men visited the club looking for a bit of company. All she had to do was to entertain them nicely, dance a bit, make them feel special and, most importantly, get them to drink a lot. All she would get was coloured water, but she had to tell the men it was a champagne cocktail. Frankie explained that the cocktail came with a coloured stick. She must keep the sticks for, at the end of the night, she would receive two and sixpence for each stick she handed in. That was her wages, she would be paid nothing extra.

"It's up to you what you do when the club shuts," he went on. "See, you could make a bit extra. What am I saying? A lot extra, especially with your looks. Come along at nine tonight and I'll show you the score. By the way, wear something nice. We only have high class girls here."

And so Anita had found herself working for Frankie. She was one of the most popular girls there. Customers would often ask for her company for the evening. She made a lot of money just drinking the coloured water, although it did mean she had to visit the lavvy on several occasions! Frankie was friendly with the taxi drivers, and they would bring customers to the club for him. They were rewarded by a generous glass of whisky, not watered down incidentally!

For a while, Anita had declined the men's offers to escort her home for something a bit extra. This, however, had changed when Omar came into the club. Omar was an Arab and threw money around as if it was water. He offered Anita fifty pounds to go back with him to the Cumberland Hotel and spend the night. She could not hold out against that. In fact, they had become good friends, despite the strange circumstances in which they had met. Anita found herself accompanying him to America, France and Rome as his guest. He lavished gifts on her and had bought her this flat.

Sylvia, hearing this story through to the end,

remarked sadly that she did not think any man would want her company for the evening.

"Nonsense!" replied her friend. "You're just feeling sorry for yourself. You're pretty when you're dressed up and wear a little make-up. Borrow this frock and come down the club with me tonight. I bet I get you fixed up. Mind you, Frankie might want to see you first. He didn't bother with me as I think he was desperate for some girls to join his club. Now he has so many applying for hostess jobs, he only chooses the best.

"What do you mean when you say that Frankie might want to see me first? Surely he'll see me when I walk in with you."

Anita sighed dramatically. "What I mean, you silly little goose, is that he might want to try you out. See how you perform." Seeing Sylvia's blank expression, she began to spell out what Frankie might want to do to satisfy himself as to Sylvia's suitability. "It's bit like Hollywood," she went on. "If you can imagine how many young, pretty and glamorous women are there, all looking for film work, how do you imagine that some get chosen while other's aren't? They get tested by a randy old film producer who tells them that sleeping with him will further their career. Most of them want to get on and so they agree to what he is offering. They hope at the end of it, a big fat contract awaits them and so the old bugger shags all the women he wants. Now do you understand what I mean?"

"Yes," replied Sylvia. "You're trying to tell me that Frankie might want to sleep with me. Is that it?"

"That's about it kid." Then seeing the frightened look that crossed Sylvia's face, she added, " But then again, he might not bother. You'll just have to wait and see, won't you?"

Chapter Eighteen

Nine o'clock found Sylvia sitting in the foyer waiting for Frankie. Her palms were sweating with fear. She needed this job badly, but how badly? Badly enough to want to sleep with him?

Anita now came out of the room having first briefed Frankie about how nervous Sylvia was.

"Chin up girl, he'll see you now." She held the door open. "Good luck," she whispered, as Sylvia stepped inside.

The interior was gloomy, lit only by a red light bulb. She saw a couch in the corner of the room next to a tiny wash basin. Peering into the gloom, Sylvia could make out the shadow of a man. So this was Frankie.

"Come in Sylvia, I won't bite," chuckled Frankie.

"Sit down and let me look at you. Very nice, very nice. Would you like a drink?" Without waiting for an answer, he took a crystal decanter full of whisky from the silver tray beside him, and proceeded to pour out two generous measures of Scotch.

Sylvia remembered her vow never to touch alcohol again. But . . . in this situation, it might help her to relax. All the time she kept telling herself she needed this job.

Frankie leaned forward in his chair. She could see him better now. He was, she guessed, in his mid-forties, not particularly good-looking, but not ugly either. He had a shock of black hair and big bushy eyebrows from under which he peered intently at her. Handing her a glass, he asked the question;

"What makes you think you're suitable for a job here?"

Sylvia jumped. She hadn't even thought about her suitability, she had just taken Anita's word for it.

"Well. I'm waiting."

Sylvia told him that she thought it was easy money for just drinking with men.

Frankie laughed at her honesty. "It's not that easy you know. Sometimes the men can get very possessive about my women," he boasted. "Sometimes we have a little trouble, not much you understand, normally when they've had a bit too much to drink." Frankie lit a cigar. "Can you dance?" he asked suddenly.

"A bit," she replied.

"Can you talk about everything and anything?"

She nodded eagerly. "Oh, yes. I love meeting

people, and talking to them too."

"What about drinking? Do you like drinking? I see you haven't touched your drink yet." Frankie motioned towards the glass which was still full.

"I don't like it very much," she confessed, " But, if it's part of the job, then I'll just have to learn to like it."

Frankie blew a cloud of smoke into the air. "Well don't worry too much about that. You don't have to drink anything, but your main job is to keep the punters happy and also to make sure that they buy lots of drinks. You have to get them to buy you cocktails. Do you think you can persuade them?"

"Of course I can." retorted Sylvia. "I can do anything if I put my mind to it."

Frankie laughed, a huge booming sound that echoed round the small room. "That's what I like to hear, a girl with a bit of spirit. Yes, I think you'll do. You speak extremely well, not common like some that have worked for me. I'm sure you'll be an asset to my club."

Thinking that the interview was now over, Sylvia got up to go.

"Hang on a minute, not so fast."

Sylvia's heart sank. This was it . . . yet again! She sat on the edge of her chair. Frankie stood up and came round the side of the table. "Stand up." he ordered.

Sylvia did as she was told.

Frankie appraised her slim figure. He ran his hand along her bare arm. Sylvia shivered. Then he lightly stroked her nipples, which were standing out under the flimsy material of the frock. "Lovely pair of tits," he said. "I wouldn't mind giving them a suck. Feel me! Go on, Feel me!" he said urgently. Taking her hand he placed it against his groin.

Sylvia's immediate reaction was to draw her hand away, but ever mindful of how much she needed this job, she kept it there. Frankie's hand closed over hers and he moved it up and down against his trousers. Next he opened his flies and pushed her hand inside. "Just play with me little," he pleaded.

Sylvia couldn't help shuddering. Memories of her father came flooding back. But she did as she was told. Meanwhile Frankie had slipped the dress down over her bust and was now sucking hungrily at her tits. Then suddenly Frankie let out a fierce groan, accompanied with a loud cry of "Oh yes! Oh yes!" Then . . . it was all over. Her hand was covered in the same white sticky substance that reminded her of her father all those years ago. Still it was over. She hoped he didn't want anything more of her. Then to her relief . . .

"You can have a wash and tidy up." Frankie offered, pointing to the wash basin and handing her a towel.

Sylvia washed her hands, adjusted her clothing, then stood waiting.

"What are you waiting for?" he barked. "Get out there and roll those punters. And try to look a bit more cheerful," he begged. "You won't have anyone wanting to buy you a drink looking like that! He pinched her cheek. "Oy vay, but you're a funny one all right. Well go on then," he said, as she didn't move. He smacked her backside heftily as she left the room.

"I must be meshugana to take her on." he mumbled to himself. "But I have a hunch about that one. I think she'll do me proud."

* * *

Sylvia sat in the club feeling decidedly uncomfortable. She felt bare as she watched the men coming in, like a prize exhibit in her black frock. She glanced around the club. Tables were placed around the sides of the room, a bar was over on the far right hand side and in the middle of the floor was a tiled dancing area with a revolving crystal ball above it. Shards of coloured lights were casting pretty patterns on the floor. Anita, as usual, was the first one to be chosen. A couple of the others were also picked up. Now there were only six of them left. Sylvia looked at the other girls who remained. They were all rather glamorous. She didn't notice the elderly white-haired man approaching her until he was nearly upon her.

"I'm sorry," he said. "I didn't mean to startle you. Would you be so kind as to let me buy you a drink?"

"Yes. that would be nice," she said, smiling up at him.

She caught sight of Anita being whirled around the dimly-lit dance floor, and her friend gave her the thumbs up sign.

The other girls seemed a bit put out by this newcomer who had been picked almost straight away.

Diane, who was by far the prettiest looking girl there with her long blonde hair and vivid blue eyes, whispered to her friend Alice. "What a bloomin' cheek. Fancy us being upstaged by that one!"

Alice replied cattily, that perhaps Sylvia was picked because of her teeth that glowed in dark. Alice was attractive too, a long curly haired red-head with a vibrant personality.

"Don't be so nasty," retorted Shirley. "She's got a gorgeous figure. One that I would die for."

The others laughed. Shirley was inclined to be on the plump side, but with her pleasant face and pleasing disposition, she was extremely popular among the clientele.

The white haired gentleman sat down at a table and ordered a 'pink champagne' for Sylvia and a bottle of bourbon for himself.

"Would you like to dance?" asked Sylvia politely.

"No, not really. I'd much rather talk to you."

"All right then," she replied, "The music is a bit too fast for me anyway."

"I can't stand loud music at the best of times. I'm more of a classical person you see."

Sylvia did see and she secretly thought that this new record by the Rolling Stones was rubbish. She reminded herself it was her job to keep the customers happy. So if he wanted to talk, then that was fine by her.

He told her his name was Hugh and that he was a member of the government.

"What does that mean exactly?" she asked.

"It means my dear," he said, whispering in her ear, "that I am a member of parliament. I have to be discreet you know."

Sylvia was shocked. What on earth was a well respected member of the government doing here? Suddenly she saw Anita trying to attract her attention. "Excuse me one moment please," she told him. "I won't be a minute."

She followed Anita to the ladies. Anita turned to her and asked "What's the old codger like then?"

"He's all right. A little bit boring, but quite nice really."

"Listen," said Anita. "If he's going to spend all evening with you, insist that he keeps buying you drinks. You won't earn anything on just one drink alone, you've got to make the punters spend their money on you. Chat 'em up a bit. Flatter them. Make them think there will be something at the end of the evening, you know . . . ?"

That evening Sylvia earned nine pounds. This was a fortune when you reckon that she had worked all week for eight pounds and fifteen shillings; here she had earned that much and more in just five hours! She mentally calculated that she must have had thirty six cocktails in order to earn all that. No wonder why she kept going to the toilet every five minutes!

Sylvia found herself looking forward to her job every evening. The other girls presented no problems once they had got to know each other. They competed with each other over who could wear the classiest frock. All this extra money meant that Sylvia could now afford to buy herself the nicest of clothes. She would go to the club in a different one every night bringing forth gasps of 'Ooohs and Ahhhs' from the others, who, determined not to be outdone, would then go out and get something new themselves. Frankie was delighted at this turn of events. Okay, his girls always looked smart, but since the arrival of Sylvia and her passion for new clothes, he found that the others were quick to follow suit. His club and reputation began to flourish as more customers than ever joined.

The weeks passed quickly. Sylvia had no desire to leave Anita's flat and the two girls got on well together considering the shaky beginning of their friendship. There was a friendly rivalry between them at the club to see who would be picked first. Anita was still the most popular, but Sylvia was a close second. She could talk to men on all levels. The club catered for a wide clientele: politicians, film stars, soldiers, sailors and ordinary everyday men seeking a way out of the humdrum boredom of life. They found Sylvia refreshing. For one thing, she looked far younger than her twenty years. For another, she could hold her own in conversation.

She had made it a policy not to accept the offers of men who wanted to leave the club with her – and plenty had. But it still didn't stop them from buying her drinks. She earned good money every evening. Anita still saw Omar, who made sure that she didn't want for anything.

Sylvia happened to say one day that she wished she could find someone as kind and thoughtful as Omar.

Anita laughed. "Don't you mean rich as well?"

"Well yes, that too. You know, I really like it here. You and I get on so well together."

"I've been meaning to talk you about that," Anita said gravely.

Sylvia felt her heart sink. "I haven't outstayed my welcome, have I?"

"No, lovey, it's nothing like that. Omar has asked me to go and live in the states with him. Well, I've agreed! I've no family left to worry about me and I know he thinks a great deal of me. I wouldn't have any worries about money; not that I've got any now. He wants to take care of me. He says he's sick and tired of my being around men, and the way they look at me. He wants me to leave that life behind and devote myself to him alone."

"I'm really happy for you, Anita, honestly. Does he want to marry you?"

Anita threw her head back and laughed. "How naive you are! You silly goose, he's already married!"

Sylvia didn't know where to look. It was not the first time she had shown herself up by her lack of knowledge of the outside world. She thought if a man showed that much interest in you, then he must want to marry you.

Anita went on. "Of course, it was an arranged marriage – what they call a marriage of convenience. He doesn't love his wife and she doesn't love him."

Sylvia looked doubtful about this. "I don't think much of a marriage like that. It's doomed from the beginning. When I marry, it's got to be for love."

"You read too many romantic novels, lovey. It's not always like that. Anyway, Omar has decided to sell this flat, so I'm afraid you'll have to find somewhere else to live. I did try asking him if you could stay here, but he wants to put the past behind him and start afresh. You do understand?" she said appealingly.

Sylvia inclined her head. Words failed her. What would she do without her friend – her friend who was always there for her, to advise her, to look after her? The thought of not having her around was unbearable.

"I'll look for somewhere tomorrow," she said, brokenly.

"I'll help you if you like," Anita offered.

Between them, they did find Sylvia another place. It was a flat in Shepherds Bush. Wisely, she had saved most of her money and was able to put down the hundred pounds deposit. The rent was ten guineas a week, which she could easily afford working at Frankie's. It was farther from the West End than she would have liked, but it was well appointed, with a small garden, double bedroom, living room, kitchen and bathroom. It was in a terraced house. The front room was a bedsit, then there was her flat, and there were two more flats upstairs. The landlord lived next door, so there were no restrictions, which pleased her.

"It's really nice Sylvia. I'm so happy for you."

Sylvia sighed. "Yes it is nice, but I'm going to miss you. You're the only family I have now. Do you really have to go?"

"It's not a question of whether I have to go or not. Omar is the best thing that ever happened to me. The fact is that I love him. I need his strength, his humour and his down-to-earthness. If I stay I will only become more and more bitter when I see the way that some men use women. I can't let that happen. I can't allow it to ruin what bit of happiness I can have with Omar. This is my big chance and I want you to be pleased for me."

"Of course I'm pleased for you. Don't mind me . . . I'm only being selfish." Sylvia hugged the other girl warmly.

It was a tearful farewell at London Airport. Anita told Sylvia that she must visit them in the States any time she wanted.

Sylvia waved from the visitor's lounge until the plane flew behind some low cloud and vanished from sight. She knew she would miss Anita for the rest of her life.

She felt suddenly very alone. Returning home, she cried until it was time to pull herself together and go to work.

Chapter Nineteen

She could hear the new tenant moving about in the room next to her bedroom. She wondered whether it were male or female. Female, she hoped, and preferably around her own age.

She went hesitantly to knock on the door. A man opened it. He was rather sweet-looking, with long fair hair and round glasses.

"Hullo," she said, her words coming out in a rush of embarrassment. "I live in the flat next to yours, and my name is Sylvia. I thought you might like a cup of coffee.

"Thanks very much! I haven't had time to pop the kettle on. As you can see I've got so much stuff and nowhere to put it. I'm just trying to make room for it all. I say, you are lucky having a flat. Do you live by yourself?"

Sylvia found out that his name was Brian and that he had just finished his degree in mathematics at Cambridge University. In the course of conversation, she happened to glance at her watch.

"God! Look at the time! I've got to run! Sorry!"

"Where are you off to at this hour of day?"

"I'm working." She flung this remark over her shoulder as she rushed towards the bathroom. "Sorry, you'll have to excuse me."

She didn't feel that she could tell Brian anything about her work for the time being. It wasn't a normal kind of job and she was not sure how he would react if he knew what she did for a living. She liked what she had seen of him, and she didn't want to jeopardise their friendship at this early stage. Maybe one day the opportunity would present itself . . . .

* * *

"Come on! You're late! Where have you been? There's a gentleman here who has asked for you especially." Frankie was cross.

Sylvia climbed the stairs to the dimly lit club. It was busy tonight. A young man, clutching a bottle of champagne came over and guided her to a table set back in the alcove. She noted with some concern that he had been drinking heavily. Still, she wasn't too worried – Frankie had bouncers waiting to eject anyone from the club at the first signs of trouble.

The man started off quite pleasantly, but his behaviour deteriorated as the evening wore on and he continued to drink. He grabbed Sylvia by the arm and pulled her up on to the dance floor. Holding her tightly, he smooched to the sound of Peter and Gordon singing 'World Without Love'. Sylvia thanked him when the record had finished and made off to sit down again. He joined her and asked if he could see her home after the club closed. Sylvia wanted to refuse as she always did, but the young man was most insistent – too insistent. As she tried to think of a way out, she saw the look of anger cross his face.

"Could you come back at three when the club closes?" she found herself saying, knowing full well that they closed at two.

"That's better, darling," he said. "After all the money I've spent on you, I think I'm entitled to something a bit more, don't you?"

Sylvia merely smiled.

When the club closed, she called out goodnight to everyone and began to descend the stairs. It was a lovely May evening. She looked around nervously, but the street was empty. She started to breathe a sigh of relief, when . . .

"Over here!"

His voice made her jump. She hadn't noticed the car waiting in the shadows. Her brain wasn't functioning as it should and she wondered what on earth she could do.

The man opened the door. "I thought you'd come out early that's why I've been waiting. Didn't think you could get rid of me that easily, did you?"

Sylvia suddenly felt scared. She looked around in the hope of seeing a taxi, but the street was deserted.

"Come on, hop in. I'll take you home."

Sylvia got into his car.

"Where to?"

"Shepherds Bush."

She watched all the familiar streets rush by. Then he took a different turning.

"This is the wrong way," she said. But he didn't answer. "Where are we going?" she asked.

He kept his eyes on the road. "I want to talk to you," he explained. Then the car slowed down.

"Where are we? What's . . . ? She was stuttering.

She looked out of the window. They were down a quiet country lane.

With one swift movement, the man flung himself over and locked her door. Then he pushed her back and began to grind his body against hers. His heavy hands grabbed at her. She could feel his hot breath, his mouth trying to find hers. She was so shocked that at first she didn't realise what was happening. Then, suddenly . . .

"Get off, Get OFF!" she screamed, turning her face, trying to push him away from her.

He was sweating. "You know you want it," he panted. Now he had her pinned properly, his hand pawing under her frock. She was powerless, she couldn't even kick out. His weight was making it hard enough for her to breathe, let alone yell.

Then, abruptly, he sat back. "I'm sorry," he said.

"I'll take you home."

For a second, it was like nothing had happened. But she looked down, saw her ripped stockings, her torn skirt, and started to cry.

Then his hand flew out again, grabbing at her breasts.

"No! she screamed."

He licked his lips, her resistance exciting him more.

She brought both hands down on his and closed her eyes to try to give her the strength to prise him off.

"I know you want me, bitch," he hissed, flooring the accelerator.

Her heart was hammering, but she knew what she had to do. As he took a sharp turn, he slowed down fractionally. Sylvia unlocked the door and yanked the handle. She tumbled out, bracing herself against hitting the ground at speed. But she felt no pain – it didn't register. All she felt was relief.

The man stopped. "Your loss, love!" he yelled. Then he screeched off.

She clambered to her feet and started walking to the main road. As she reached it, she looked behind her and saw a taxi cruising along. Hailing it, she climbed in and gave the driver instructions to take her home.

She fumbled for her keys and unlocked the front door. Stumbling down the hallway, she fished out the second key to unlock the door to her flat. She collapsed sobbing on the sofa. A while later she took a bath to try and put the episode behind her.

*   *   *

That night there was a fierce thunderstorm. A huge streak of lightning, followed by a clap of thunder, lit Sylvia's bedroom. She was frightened and put her head under the bedcovers to try to drown out the noise. It was no good, she'd have to get up. Outside on the landing a light was showing from beneath Brian's door. She decided to see if he was all right. She knocked on the door and it was opened almost immediately.

"Sorry to disturb you, only I got scared and thought I'd make a drink. Then I saw your light on and wondered if you'd like one, too," she said falteringly.

Brian looked at her and saw her puffy face, her bloodied arms and legs.

He opened the door wider. "Why don't you come in and I'll make you a drink?" he said. "You look as if you could do with one."

He poured the coffee, then said, "Do you want to talk about it?"

The words poured out. Brian interrupted her. "We ought to call the police," he said.

"No, please don't. It was nothing. I don't want them involved."

Brian was insistent. "You've got to. That animal's a rapist. If he can do that to you, then he can do it to someone else.

Sylvia knew that he was right. But she couldn't afford to get mixed up with the police. They would want to ask all sorts of questions . . . Where do you work? Why were you out so late? No, she couldn't involve them.

The storm raged as they sat and talked on into the early hours of morning. By her watch, Sylvia could see it had just turned four; she said she felt she ought to go back to her own room now. Brian offered to let her stay with him if she still felt afraid. She readily agreed and felt no fear as they both got into bed. He pulled the covers up around her and she slept like a baby.

When morning came, she found herself snuggled up in Brian's arms. She looked into his sleeping face and found herself wondering why he hadn't taken advantage of her. He woke up then and answered the question he could see in her eyes.

"I'm gay!" he explained. "I don't fancy women at all. I like their company, but that's all. There now, I'm glad I've told you. I had a boyfriend in Cambridge, but it didn't work out." His face looked sad.

She found herself telling him about her life, her job; in fact, all the things that had happened to her – including her father.

"You poor thing," he said when she had finished. "I wish I were normal; I could look after you. I'd really like to get married, but the thought of making love to a woman repulses me."

Sylvia couldn't help laughing at the look of disgust on his face. What a change to meet someone like this! It was not her usual experience with men. They all wanted something from her; but she had decided that the way of life she now led meant that she was taking something from them. She wasn't to realise until later that she was in some way seeking revenge on her father.

For the next six weeks, until the day when Brian left to go home to Wales, they were close friends. Sylvia would let him use her perfume. She would make him up on occasions and lend him her frocks. He never wore them outside, but they understood each other implicitly. On the odd occasion when she wasn't working, he would take her to his club. The Robin Hood in Kings Road, near to where she had once lived, was a gay club. She enjoyed meeting all his friends, but drew the line at being chatted up by some of the butch women. One in particular, Kath, had taken quite a shine to Sylvia. She had brown hair which stuck up in little short spikes.

"I like you Kath, but I'm just not that way inclined," she told her, after yet another night of being pursued by the unshakeable Kath. Turning to Brian, she said, "I thought you said they didn't chat up people who aren't gay? I thought you said they left straight people alone?"

Brian, his arms wrapped around his latest conquest, didn't seem to want to hear her question. He was too engrossed with having fun himself.

But Sylvia continued to go with him, as on the whole, they were a good crowd. Anyway, she didn't find Kath that repulsive, in fact she was quite a nice person when she had learned to take no for an answer.

She cried on the day that Brian left, but he promised to write regularly. One day he might even come back and marry her. He really was such a gentle man!

Chapter Twenty

The landlord appeared in the garden and tapped on her window. "Phone call for you!" he shouted.

Sylvia wondered who earth could be ringing her here. The only person who knew where she was was her old friend June. They still kept in touch, although Sylvia had not seen her since she had run away from home to Blackpool in 1960.

She picked up the phone.

"Miss Short?"

"Yes? Speaking?"

"I'm afraid you don't know me," the voice said, "but my name is Littlejohn of Littlejohn and Carter, solicitors. I have some bad news for you I'm afraid. Your father died in February. I'm sorry we haven't contacted you sooner, but we have only just found out where you are. Could you come to 121 Peckham Hill Street sometime this week to discuss the estate? Your father died intestate, and you and your adopted brother, as next of kin, stand to benefit from the sale of the house and its contents."

Sylvia said that she would come along later that day. She was shocked and relieved at the same time. First her mother, now her father. She wondered what he had died of.

Four-thirty found her sitting with Hugh Littlejohn in his office. Apparently, Mr. Short had died in the 'Gowlett Arms' of a coronary thrombosis. One minute he had been sitting on a stool with a drink in his hand. The next minute he had collapsed onto the floor where he had died almost immediately. According to the coroner, he had ruined his kidneys after a lifetime of drinking.

"Your brother has found alternative accommodation," the solicitor continued, "and he has stated that he wishes the house to be sold. As you are under twenty-one, we have to appoint executors on your behalf. Are you agreeable that the house be sold?"

Sylvia was silent for a moment. Just thinking about the place made her shudder. She could never go back there again.

"No," she said finally in a low voice. "I don't want the house, thank you. But I would like to see it before it's sold."

Mr Littlejohn peered over his glasses. "I think that can be arranged. Now, have you any objections to

your Uncle John and Aunt Eva acting as your repre-
sentatives? All that means," he added, "is that you will
be notified when all the legalities have gone through.
You should have a nice little sum to put by. We are
thinking of putting it on the market for £3,500. By the
time all the fees and expenses have been met, you are
looking at something in the region of £1,000."

A thousand pounds! This was a small fortune.
Sylvia could hardly believe her luck.

Leaving the solicitor's office, she decided to take a
look around her old haunts. It was ages since she had
last been in Peckham. She turned the corner slowly
where Jones and Higgins still stood and walked slowly
up Rye Lane. All the old familiar shops were still
there. Memories came flooding back. Reaching the
top near the Heaton Arms, she crossed over the road
and walked past Gloria's aunt's baker's shop. Gloria
was nowhere to be seen. Things must have changed in
the four years since she had lived here.

On she walked, passing the end of Amott Road. She
began to feel excited as she reached number 39, where
June lived. She rang the bell once, twice, then again
more impatiently. No answer! To her disappointment
no one appeared to be in. Then a neighbour from
across the road, whom she didn't recognise, shouted
out that they had just gone on holiday.

Her steps took her around the corner to the old
house. It looked unkempt, dirty even. She let herself
in through the side gate. The garden was in need of a
good weeding. She glanced up at her bedroom
window at the top of the house. She could still hear

her screams of pain when she was being beaten – or worse . . ...

She continued to the top of the road to the little park at Goose Green, where she had played on the swings all those years ago. To her disappointment she noticed that Fred's cafe on the East Dulwich Road was boarded up. How she had loved playing that juke box there on the way to school. Further on she came to Peckham Rye Park, and stopped in amazement. The annual fair was here again. Her fingers went to the chain that she still wore around her neck with the medallion on it. She had kept this memento through the toughest times, even in hospital – although there, she had been made to take if off and hand it over for safekeeping. She smiled ruefully when she considered that injunction from the authorities' point of view: they must have thought that she might see fit to hang herself with it.

Her footsteps quickened as she made towards the fair. Would Danny be there? Would he still remember her? Had he got his half of the medallion, too? Would he, dreadful thought, be married? He would be about twenty-three now. All these thoughts crowded through her mind.

Finally she was standing near the rows of caravans. Men with rippling muscles were pitching the various tents. It was as she stood watching them that she was spotted by a dark-haired young man – a good-looking young man with the same even white teeth, big brown eyes and long dark hair curling over his collar into the back of his neck.

"Is it really you, my little Sylvia? Why, you're all grown up now!" Danny beamed at her.

"Danny!" she screamed with delight. "How are you? Oh, I never thought I would see you again! How's your Mum? Tell me everything!" Her words tumbled over each other.

Danny led her over to a caravan which was far larger than the one she remembered.

"This is where we live now," he said proudly, opening the door. "Mother, we have a visitor."

Rosa came bustling out of the kitchen; she gasped and then took her into a bear hug. "I don't believe it! How are you? It's so good to see you. Sit down," she ordered. "I'll make a cup of Rosa's special and we can talk. I want to hear all your news. We looked for you every June, but you never came. Danny here was sad. He thought you were special." She smiled at her son, who was now looking decidedly embarrassed at his mother's betrayal of his secret feelings.

So they sat and talked, and Sylvia told them all about herself and everything that had happened, finishing off by telling them about her father and how she had come to be here today.

Rosa had a piece of news of her own: Meg had died the previous year. It was the cold winter that had done it. Then she chuckled as she remembered how the old woman had wanted to be buried with her clay pipe and how they had complied with her wishes.

"But now," she added, "I must run along. I'm sure you two young people have a lot to talk about. You won't want me standing here listening."

There was a moment's silence between them as they were left alone. Then Sylvia, raising her head to meet Bobby's eyes, saw him standing there beside her in the thin sunshine of that summer evening, the thick black hair curling to his shoulders.

"Well, Sylvia?" he said, coming to sit beside her. He touched her nose with his finger, in the gesture that she remembered so well. The next moment his arms were around her, her composure was shattered into a thousand wavering pieces and the tears came at last. There, in the caravan, hidden from prying eyes, he held her close and kissed her, gently at first, and then with passion. And she returned his kisses.

"Oh Danny, I've never forgotten you, even after all these years. But something is wrong. You look pale, thinner somehow . . ."

Danny made light of it. "Just a touch of asthma, that's all." But his speech was peppered with coughs. As he looked at Sylvia, the love was plain on his face. Sylvia felt her stomach contract. Something was changing. Danny leant close. His lips brushed hers and then Sylvia knew what had changed. She loved him.

Afterwards, gazing into each other's eyes, there was no need for words. Danny made as if to say something, but she hushed him by placing her fingers against his lips.

After they had lain there for some time, she sat up and said that she ought to think about getting back.

"Surely you're not leaving now? You can't!" he said incredulously. Sylvia gazed deep into his eyes; but she saw that the future was not mirrored there – yet.

"I have to go now," she said.

"But, Sylvia, you can't do this! I love you."

She came and touched his cheek. "I know where to find you. One day, when the time is right, I may return."

There was something in the way that she looked at him, that made him hesitate.

Then he said, "I am ill, the hospital give me five years at the most."

"What!" the words screeched out of her. She crumpled into a chair. It didn't seem real. Danny was twenty three, no age to die.

"Tell me you're lying? Tell me this is just a trick to keep me here?"

But as she looked at him she saw something in his face. Something he'd never shown before. Doubt.

"I wouldn't trick you Sylvia. This is no joke. But . . . I won't make you stay. What is the point if I am going to die." He walked over and plucked a single red rose from the vase on the table. He slid it between her fingers. "Keep this with you," he told her. "Remember me and never forget that I love you."

"I'll stay if you want me. Danny can you hear me?"

His lips stretched into a smile and she took his hand. I love you, Danny," she said.

"I love you too," he whispered to her.

"Come back and live with me," she begged.

"I have to stay and carry on the family tradition for as long as I can," he replied.

"Very well then. I'll come back to you when I have finalised all my outstanding arrangements. It shouldn't take long. Give me three months at the most and I'll be back. Here, take this, just in case you need me urgently."

Danny took her phone number and placed it in his pocket. "Don't worry Sylvia. I'm as tough as old boots. I'll make it . . . and so will we.

Chapter Twenty One

Sylvia felt very saddened at leaving Danny. It had not been an easy decision. What she did know was that everything she had ever loved in the past had been taken away from her, and she didn't want the same thing to happen now. She knew she loved Danny; she had done so from the time she had first met him when she was a young girl. In her room, she hugged herself tightly remembering his warm caresses, his dark brown eyes burning intensely into her own. "Oh, Danny," she whispered. "I hope that you understand why I had to leave you. Just have faith in me that I will return."

For two days she moped around the flat with no inclination to go to work. It was the need for money which forced her back.

Frankie was not amused. Sylvia looked at his face, which was ugly when he was cross.

"Where the hell have you been? Thanks to you, the takings have gone right down!" He waved away her protests and told her to get upstairs immediately. So she returned to the life she had begun to know so well. She went home that evening filled with hope that it would not be for much longer.

A week later the shrill ringing of the telephone woke her. It was Rosa. Danny had taken a turn for the worse. Sylvia tried to get there as quickly as possible. As she walked down the corridor, a nurse came towards her.

"Are you Sylvia?"

Sylvia nodded.

"We've been expecting you. But . . . I'm sorry . . ." her voice trailed away. Sylvia felt her legs buckle beneath her. She was too late. Danny had died peacefully only a few minutes before.

Rosa appeared, she looked old and tired. "He's gone," she wailed. "My Danny's gone." She clasped Sylvia to her, then stroking her hair she told her that Danny had cancer, a brain tumour. "There was nothing more they could do for him," she said brokenly. "But he loved you Sylvia. I was holding his hand before he slipped away and those were the last words he whispered to me."

Sylvia tried to be strong for Rosa's sake, but the tears came and then the heartache. How would she live without him? Then she remembered.

By now it had lost its fragrance and was a little tattered, but the fragile petals of her rose still clung to the bud, just as Danny had clung on to life. As she clung to the rose she knew he would always be there with her.

*　*　*

It was a couple of months later that she fainted while at work. Frankie was concerned and sent her home in a taxi with orders not to come back until she felt better.

She did feel ill. She had not had a period last month, but she blamed it on the fact that she had a couple of boils on her private parts, which last night had burst after she had bathed in very hot water. She looked at herself in the mirror and noticed ugly green veins running down her breasts. Slowly the realisation dawned on her: she was going to have a baby! But how? Whose was it? Then she smiled and a warm glow filled her body. It was Danny's. Yes, there could be no doubt about it. It had to be. Well, at least she would have something to remind her of him – a permanent reminder!

Her happiness lasted until she thought about the implications of bringing up a child single-handed. Still, other people managed so why shouldn't she? She would have to finish at Frankie's when the pregnancy became obvious. Then where would all the money come from to pay for the flat and all the other little luxuries that she had grown to expect? This wasn't the time to dwell on things like that. She had to make arrangements to go to the hospital. She was delighted to think that at long last she would have something of her own to love and take care of.

The hospital confirmed that she was three months' pregnant; and a bed was booked up to be made available at the time of her confinement, at St. Mary's Hospital, Paddington. They remarked that she was very small, but assured her that first babies are normally quite tiny.

Sylvia threw herself into her work, determined to make as much money as she could to save for the baby. Every week she could be found scouring the shops and markets buying something for it. At first she had thought that she would like a boy who would look just like his father. But on reflection, she decided that a girl would be more appropriate if she were to bring it up herself. Boys could be a lot more trouble!

It was on a shopping expedition to Piccadilly that she bumped into a face from the past. She had alighted from the tube and was walking through the tunnel when she heard the strains of a song:

"Don't be cruel, uel, uel, to a heart that's true." An Elvis song! Something about the voice was familiar.

She walked quickly to the end of the tunnel, and there he was . . . Ian. A little older, extremely thinner, but definitely Ian! An old guitar and a cap with a few pennies in it, lay in front of his feet. She walked up to him. He stared through her. Realisation dawned that he hadn't recognised her.

She touched his arm. He flinched away and then . . .

"Who are you? Come from the Welfare have you? Leave me alone. Go Away!"

"Ian. It's me, Sylvia," she said.

Ian peered at her. "Sylvia who? From where?" he mumbled incoherently.

"From Belmont."

Now that she had the opportunity to see him up close, she noticed that he was as thin as a rake – his clothes just hung off him. His face looked grey and drawn. It was as if the light had disappeared from his eyes. Then to Sylvia's astonishment, he began blubbering like a baby. Fishing in her handbag, she drew out a tissue and handed it to him.

He blew his noise loudly. "Oh, Sylvia." He stumbled and would have fallen if she had not put her hand out to steady him.

"What's the matter Ian? Are you drunk? What on earth's up with you?"

Tears fell down his cheeks again. "I can't tell you." Then shouting, "I CAN'T TELL YOU!..." his voice faded into a whisper. "You'd be disgusted. You'd reject me just like everybody else has."

"If you can't tell me, then I won't be able to help you, will I?" she said, in a soothing tone. "Come on Ian. I was your friend once. I can be your friend again if you'll only let me. Trust me," she begged, looking into his face.

"Trust you?" he spat. "I don't trust anyone!"

Sylvia could see that he was in no mood to be reasoned with. She started to walk away.

"Wait . . . "

She turned towards him.

"Yes?"

"Look, I'm sorry."

"That's okay, but I'm still willing to listen. I know, why don't we go for a coffee?"

"Can't," he mumbled, shuffling his feet. "Haven't got any money. Look," he pointed to the hat. "There's not even enough in there to buy one cup let alone two.

"Don't worry about that, it's my treat." Sylvia tucked her arm comfortably underneath his and they proceeded to Lyon's Corner House.

Over cups of coffee and slices of walnut bread, Ian's story began to unfold. When he left Belmont, he had felt in charge of his life. He was going places. He went to stay with a friend in London who fixed him up with a job. It was only in a snack bar, but it was better than nothing. The money wasn't good, so he helped himself by stealing out of the till. Then he got caught, his friend threw him out and he found himself on the streets. He began to hang around the numerous arcades in Piccadilly hoping that some money would fall through the slots. One day as he stood there, he felt someone watching him. He turned round and noticed a man staring at him. Then the man winked and gestured to Ian to follow him outside.

"How old are you?" The man addressed Ian.

"Twenty two." Ian replied.

"Pity," came the reply. "I like them younger."

"Like them younger for what?"

"Oh come on, you can't be that stupid surely! For sex of course."

Robert Dyas

Southampton Tel :02380330275

29/11/2002 12:01   A00106   T02-007076
                                    £

0000000123787 UNIC WIND UP RA   9.99
Total To Pay   £9.99

Cash Tendered   £10.00
Change   0.01

Thank you, please call again.
VAT No: GB216093678
www.robertdyas.co.uk

The Works

Unit 26 The Marlands Shopping
Centre Southampton SO14 7SJ
Tel No:02380 220393
VAT No:555 2619 34

DATE: 29/11/2002 TIME: 13:54
TILL: 0102   NO: 10245196
CASHIER: SHEILA

DESCRIPTION	£

Dinasaurs Rd Discove   1.25 C
Batteries Double AA   1.00 B

2 PC. TOTAL   £2.25

CASH   £2.50

Change   £0.25

VAT B 17.50% (£1.00) : £0.15
VAT C 0.00% (£1.25) : £0.00

" MANAGERS SPECIAL "
SAVE 60% ON THE ESSENTIAL BOND
NOW ONLY £4.99
(LIMITED PERIOD ONLY)

Ian couldn't believe his ears. He'd heard of woman selling their bodies for sex. But men . . .! He couldn't lie and say he wasn't interested. He thought that here was the solution to his problems. He could earn money and get a place to live. Anything would be better than hanging around arcades during the day and sleeping in a doorway at night. He told the man that he might be interested. The man said that he could come home with him anyway and he would fix him up with some contacts.

Ian went with him to his flat which was palatial in every sense of the word. The man paid him to stay the night. The following morning he took Ian out and lavished new clothes on him, before introducing him to his contacts. Ian soon found himself at Piccadilly Circus tube station, prostituting himself. He always lied about his age, telling his clients that he was fifteen. He'd been advised to do so. He built up a successful clientele that way. He soon found that he had enough money to put a deposit down on a flat and finally things were looking up for him.

"But what went wrong?" Sylvia interrupted. "I mean, look at you now? Surely . . . "

"No. Let me finish." Ian continued. "I was invited to many parties, influential parties. One night I saw a young boy, there. He couldn't have been any more than thirteen. He had a syringe in his hand and was injecting himself. I asked him what it was. He told me that it was something that made him feel good and did I want to try some. It was heroin and I got hooked. Then I started snorting cocaine. Now . . . " he looked at Sylvia. "I'm an addict. I need money to feed my habit. I had to give up my flat, because of my addiction and now I'm back on the streets, selling my body to subsidise my drugs. No Sylvia, don't look at me like that! I knew you wouldn't understand. I'm a rent boy. Do you hear me? A rent boy! Now do you despise me?" his voice broke.

"Oh, Ian. I wish I could help you."

"I don't need your help. There's no need to waste your pity on me. I'm happy when I'm taking drugs. They keep me warm on a cold night. They help me to forget where I am or what I am doing. Keep your sympathy!"

She took his cold hands in hers and tried to chaff some warmth into them. "Look at me Ian. Look at me," she ordered.

His face turned to hers.

"I've done some wrong things too. Just like you. I found it hard to survive on a pittance they call a wage."

"But I bet you haven't sold your body."

"Yes I have. Oh yes I have. I'm not proud of it either. I was going to put it all behind me and settle down . . ." her voice faded.

"Go on then. Tell me what happened."

Sylvia told him about the things that had happened to her since they last met including working at the night club. Then how she found Danny only to loose him again. "And now I'm pregnant," she finished.

"What are you going to do now?"

"I shall try to carry on working until the baby is due.

After that, I don't know what will happen. I suppose I'll have to live off the state like countless others . . . But wait . . . I've got an idea!"

"What's that?"

"Why don't you come and live with me? Sort yourself out, get off drugs. I'll help you."

"It won't be easy, coming off drugs I mean. I've tried it numerous times before and always end up back on them."

"Yes I know. But this time you'll have a place to stay. A warm bed to sleep in. Well a couch really. But that's got to be better than sleeping rough. Think about it, won't you?"

"Thanks a lot for the offer. You're a true friend. Give me your address and I'll come round later today. I've just got a bit of business to sort out first, then I'll come round. Say about six o'clock?"

Sylvia wrote her address on her a piece of paper and handed it to Ian. "I mean what I say. Come and stay for as long as you want."

Thanks Sylvia, Thanks a lot. I'll make it up to you . . . promise."

He got up to go. Sylvia pulled him towards her and gave him a kiss. "Pooh! You stink. First thing I'm going to do is run you a hot bath. Can't have you going around smelling like that!"

"Thanks again." Ian walked towards the door. He turned and waved before being swallowed up in the teaming throng of people all heading towards Leicester Square.

Sylvia waited. He didn't turn up, not that night, nor

the night after. A week later a policeman stood on her doorstep with a scrap of paper that Sylvia recognised immediately. It was the same paper that she had given to Ian with her address on.

"We found this in his pocket. It was the only form of identification that he had."

"Where is he? Is he hurt? Can I see him?"

The policeman ignored her questions. "Did you know this person?"

Did! Did! The past tense. "Yes, I know him. He's a friend of mine. Why?"

"Has he got any family?"

"I don't know. Look officer, what's all this about?"

"I'm sorry to have to tell you this but there's no kind way to put it. Your friend was found dead in some toilets at Piccadilly Circus."

Sylvia gave a gasp of horror.

" We can't be sure but we think it may have been a drug overdose. A syringe was found near to the body."

Sylvia was stunned. Not her friend! He was going to live with her! She was going to help him!

"I'm really sorry Miss." said the policeman, noting her pale face. "Are you all right?"

"I don't know. It's all come as a bit of a shock. I just can't believe it. I was only talking to him last week. We had made plans for him to come and live here. I was going to help wean him off his habit." Sylvia burst into tears.

"There now," said the policeman. "I'm sure you could do with a hot cup of sweet tea. That's always good for shock. My old mum told me that."

He was only trying to be sympathetic, but the last thing Sylvia felt like was a cup of tea!

"I'll be all right in a minute officer. Thank you for letting me know. I just wish there was something I could do to help."

The officer omitted to mention that Ian's body was puncture with needle marks, including his feet which he had been injecting also having run out of veins on the rest of his body. Personally, he thought it was a blessed relief for the poor chap.

"Well, if you're sure that's all," Sylvia said. "I must get on."

"Sorry to have taken up your time," the officer apologised. If you need anything, help or advice, anything, just look me up at the station." He handed her a card with his name and badge number on.

"Thank you officer, you've been very kind." Sylvia closed the door.

She grieved for Ian just as she had for Danny. They were both so young. But now she had another life to think of . . . the baby. She would make sure that it wouldn't want for anything.

Chapter Twenty Two

The months flew by. She asked her landlord if she would be able to stay on after she had had the baby, and he had raised no objections. Indeed, he had no reason to, for she made an ideal tenant. She kept her flat clean and tidy, she was quiet – and most importantly, she paid her rent on time.

One day she found Frankie looking at her with concern. He asked if she was all right.

"Of course I am!" she snapped. "Why do you ask?"

"Well, it's just that you appear to be putting on weight. The customers are saying that you don't seem to be your normal self lately. What's happened to you? You used to be our most popular girl, now hardly anyone asks for you."

It was true, her earnings had dropped drastically and that was a worry. She couldn't very well leave and start an ordinary job with the baby's birth imminent. She supposed she had been extremely fortunate to have got away with it for as long as she had without Frankie finding out. Now she felt she was obliged to tell him.

A look of sheer incredulity flickered over his face.

"Why on earth didn't you do something about it?"

"I didn't want to," she replied stubbornly. "I want to keep it."

"Well, I think you're a very silly young lady. You could have had anything you wanted. Now," he spread his hands in a gesture of exasperation, "you will have to leave. I'm afraid I can't let you go on working here in your condition. It's not good for business."

It was the moment that Sylvia had been dreading. What was she going to do?

Underneath that gruff exterior, Frankie had a heart. He gave her fifty pounds out of his own pocket, 'just to help you on you way, you understand?' He waved her expressions of gratitude away and shook his head as he watched her walk down the road. He doubted that he would find another girl as popular as she had been. What a waste! Besides, he had really liked the girl. Then he turned and slowly climbed the stairs.

★   ★   ★

Sylvia was alone again. Anita had gone, so had Brian, Danny and Ian. She felt afraid, with not a friend in the world. The baby was due in March, which was only six weeks away. She wondered how she could earn some extra money at this late stage.

She sat down on the same bench in Hyde Park where she had encountered Anita nearly two years previously, and let her thoughts drift back to how all this had started. Presently, a man who was standing by the Serpentine approached.

"You look as if you could do with some company."

"Go away!" she said.

"I say! There's no need to be unfriendly. I was only trying to be helpful."

Sylvia looked at him long and hard. "Just what do you mean by 'helpful' ?"

She listened to the story she had heard so many times before in the club. The man was lonely. He was in London on business and needed some female companionship.

Then her mind began to work. Why not? At least she could continue to earn money. It wouldn't be for her, she decided, but for the baby. She smiled at him encouragingly.

"Well, I'm sure we can come to some arrangement," she told him.

Back at the flat, she tore off her clothes, wanting to get it over with as quickly as possible. He touched her swollen tummy.

"You're pregnant?"

She nodded.

"That's nice. I like pregnant women. I think they have a certain bloom about them. Don't worry, I'll be very gentle." And he was.

Five pounds was a lot of money for ten minutes, she thought to herself as she showed him out. She calculated how much she could accumulate if she charged five pounds a time. No, perhaps five was too much. She would charge three pounds, but if she thought they looked as if they had money, then she would up the price.

Night time found Sylvia standing on the corner at the junction of Bayswater Road and Queensway.

At the end of the evening, she had managed to make fifteen pounds. She argued again that it was for the baby, and not for herself. Her conscience appeased, she returned home, ran a bath and scrubbed herself from top to bottom in the near scalding water.

The next night, she was back on the same corner. Men would come up and exchange a few words. Some thought the price too high, others were a little more interested.

A car cruised by. A man wound down the window. "How much?"

Sylvia looked at the car, it was a Porshe. She looked at the man. A bit young, very good looking, nicely dressed. "Five pounds," she replied.

"Hop in then."

As soon as Sylvia got into the car, she realised she had made a mistake. Oh, yes, the man was pleasant enough. But he was too good looking to have to pay for sex, she decided. She had a gut feeling that this was no ordinary man just looking for sex on the side. She was right.

He drove miles, way out of London and finally stopped at a house in Osterley. All throughout the journey, he had hardly said a word. Now he pulled up and opened the car door.

"It's quite a long way to come," she ventured to say.

"Well we're here now," he said. "Come on in."

He took a key from his pocked and unlocked the front door. The lights were on and music was coming from a room.

"He we are then," he said, flinging open a door. The door led to a bedroom and in the bedroom were four other men. They looked at Sylvia, licked their lips and laughed. Then they began to talk in a foreign language.

"Please can you speak in English," she appealed to them. "I can't understand what you're saying."

"Just as well, 'cos you wouldn't want to know," one of them said, coming over to stand beside her.

"Bags I first," said one.

"No me," cried another one.

"Well I think it should be me. I picked her up," said the young man whose car she had got into.

This wasn't exactly what Sylvia had planned. She guessed what they wanted to do to her. Not if she had anything to do with it, she vowed. She started to scream. One of the men came over and smacked her around the face.

"Stop it!" he hissed.

By now, Sylvia was very frightened. She started to cry. Another man came over.

"Don't cry," he said. "We're not going to hurt you."

"I just want to go home," she whimpered.

"Shut up! I said, SHUT UP!" his friendly tone vanished. He pulled his hand back and hit her hard across the head.

Sylvia fell to the ground. She thought they were going to kill her. Never in all the time that she had slept with men for money had she ever been so frightened. Or indeed been aware of the risks. Up until now, she had been lucky with her clients. She needed the money for the baby, but now she would be lucky to escape with her life. She knew they were all going to take turns in raping her.

She tried one last time. "Please let me go. I promise I won't say anything. Just please let me go," she pleaded.

"Oh. All right then," decided the man who had picked her up. He opened the front door and pushed her out. "You're nothing but a little slag. Do you honestly think I would pay you money? he asked incredulously. You'd have to pay me, you ugly bitch!"

Sylvia started walking down the path thankful that she had escaped so easily. Then she heard footsteps running behind her. The men were bearing down on her. She took to her heels and ran as fast as she could screaming at the top of her voice. This must have frightened them off for when she turned round again, they were gone. She still continued running until she came to the main road and could see the tube station ahead. She breathed a sigh of relief. It would certainly make her think twice next time she went out to pick someone up!

But the next night she went out just the same. A bit more cautiously this time. She had found a client, one that was elderly, and so in her book, more trustworthy, and was just about to get into his car, when two policemen came up to them. "Do you know this woman?" they asked the driver.

The man became flustered, knowing what having the label 'Kerb Crawler' attached to him could do to his marriage and reputation:

"No, Officer," he replied, "I don't. I was only driving home when this young lady accosted me."

The story was a pack of lies and they knew it. They had watched his car cruising around for the past hour. However, they were not interested in him, only the girl. So they let him go. As they were on the beat and didn't have a patrol car with them, they flagged down a taxi.

"Get in!" one of them ordered.

Sylvia was pushed roughly into the back of the taxi. Before they could get in after her, she had opened the opposite door to the kerb and ran off down Queensway. The policemen pursued her until suddenly she was grabbed by a man who was watching the chase. He held on to her until the policemen arrived.

"Let me go! Let me go!" she kicked out at the man.

"Not likely," he said. "Here you are then," he told

the policemen when they had caught up with her. "Is there a reward for capturing her?"

"Sorry mate. But thanks anyway."

Sylvia, was taken down to Notting Hill Gate police station, where they took her fingerprints and ran a check to see if she had any previous convictions for soliciting.

"Nothing on this one . . . yet." The policeman's words hung on the "yet".

She had to make a statement and was then told that she was being arrested on suspicion of soliciting and would be appearing before Marylebone magistrates court in the morning. Meanwhile she would have to spend the night in the cells as there was nobody she knew of who could arrange bail for her. She was told that she was allowed one phone call. Did she have anyone whom she wished to contact?

"No, no one," was all she could reply.

She was taken to a cell and given a blanket. The older policeman told her that he hoped she would have time to reflect on the graveness of the offence, before shutting the door and turning the key.

Sylvia sat down wearily on the rubber mattress. How she could have sunk to such depths, she wondered, as she looked around her at the cracked toilet in the corner and the barred windows above. She wrapped the blanket about her and lay down, feeling chilled. For hours sleep would not come; then, scarcely had she dozed off than she was awoken again, and saw the grey dawn creeping through the window.

She felt her legs turning to jelly as she stood in the dock. The magistrate was very fierce looking and delivered a long lecture about the dangers of prostitution, which made Sylvia think about her life. She now recognised that she had a duty to look after her child. It was useless to deny the charge, so she pleaded guilty; but she begged for leniency when she was asked if she had anything to say.

The magistrate reflected for a moment; then he cleared his throat.

"As this is your first offence," he said, "I shall not be too hard on you. You will be fined ten pounds. Did I hear the officer mention that you had no family?"

"Yes," she whispered.

"Speak up, girl! I can't hear you!"

"Yes. I have no family."

"Very well." He briefly consulted with his colleagues. "I hereby declare that you will also be placed on probation for a period of one year. That means that you will report to a probation officer at such times deemed necessary by her. If you do not comply with the rules as stipulated, then you will be returned to this court and a more severe penalty will await you. Is that understood?"

Sylvia swallowed before replying: "Yes, sir. And thank you."

"That is all. You may go. But report first to reception, who will arrange for you to see your probation officer."

Chapter Twenty Three

It was the best thing that could have happened to her, as it turned out. The probation officer, who was called Miss Ebberington, immediately took Sylvia under her wing. She was a small woman with white hair and rosy thread-veined cheeks. Her manner was kindly, although she would stand for no nonsense. She had seen girls like Sylvia before. Some saw the error of their ways and made an effort to reform; others were no-hopers, destined for a life of crime. In Sylvia's case, it was apparent that the root of her problems lay far back.

Over the next few weeks, Miss Ebberington worked very hard for Sylvia. Once she was in possession of all the facts, she went first to Ivydale Road to have a word with Sylvia's Auntie Eva and Uncle John. She had hoped that they might offer to help with the baby when it was born, but she came away disgusted by their lack of support. Undaunted, she made all the monetary arrangements concerning the flat and, with the help of the WRVS, Sylvia now had nearly everything she needed for the baby, including a weekly allowance, which she had not known she was entitled to.

Together they went shopping for a pram for the baby. Anyone who saw them out together would have thought them proud mother and daughter. In fact Sylvia secretly wished she could have been her mother. This kind lady had helped her so much.

"My feet are killing me!" Sylvia turned to Miss Ebberington. "Do you think we could stop and have a cup of coffee.

"Of course we can my dear. How thoughtless of me."

They found a small coffee shop and sat down at a table by the window.

"That's better," said Sylvia, as the waiter bought two steaming cups of coffee and a toasted tea-cake each. She closed her hands around the warmth of the cup and leant forward. "Do you think I could tell you something?

"Yes Sylvia. You know you can tell me anything."

"Well . . . This is a sort of confession."

"Yes, go on, I'm listening."

"Do you remember when we first met?"

"How could I forget?"

"Well the judge told me afterwards that you were going to help me. I remember thinking that it was more of a punishment than help. You introduced yourself after the court case, and told me that you were going to be my probation officer. I thought to myself that you were another 'do-gooder'." Sylvia smiled. "I really thought I knew it all at my age. You introduced yourself at the court case, and told me emphatically that must come and see you regularly. Regularly, meant at least once a week for the next year. So this to me seemed like a life sentence. I was very much in awe of you, although at least I respected my peers. You looked so stern and unsmiling that I was afraid of you. I made a mental note to try to turn up for our sessions together otherwise I had no doubt that I would be locked up for life and the key thrown away. But now, I just wanted you to know how much I appreciate all that you're doing for me. I don't know how I could have managed without you," she finished.

"Well now, that was a long speech dear. My job is to try to help people wherever necessary, and, if only one person is helped by me, then my job is fulfilled. I know you are not a bad girl at heart. Please remember, we still have a long way to go yet."

"I don't mind, really. I just wanted you to know, that's all. By the way, have you got any children?"

"Regretfully I haven't Sylvia. I never married. Oh, there was someone whom I loved deeply many years ago, but . . ."

"Go on." Sylvia urged.

Miss Ebberington's eyes misted over. "He was an

airline pilot in the war. One day I received a telegram to say that he was missing in action. I haven't heard any more since that day."

"But he could still be alive, couldn't he?"

"I doubt it my dear. I very much doubt it after all this time."

Sylvia thought it would be wonderful if her lover came back one day. Perhaps they would be too late to have children, after all Miss Ebberington was getting on in years. But still they could live happily ever after, she reasoned. Yes, she liked a story with a happy ending. Besides she thought Miss Ebberington deserved some happiness herself after bringing so much to others.

Miss Ebberington looked at her watch. "Goodness me! Look at the time! I must get back to Dinah, she will be wondering where I am."

Dinah was a black Labrador that usually accompanied her mistress everywhere. She would lie obediently on a blanket on the back seat of Miss Ebberington's car. She was old, but so intelligent and very alert. Recently she had had a stroke so was confined to the peace and quiet of home. Miss Ebberington didn't think if fair to excite her by taking her around on her travels all the time now. Sylvia knew just how attached to the dog she was. It just went to show that Miss Ebberington was a good person. Why? Because all nice people love animals.

* * *

Then Miss Ebberington's own leave came up. She was off to her sister's in the Cotswolds for a week of relaxation.

"Now, don't you go having that baby while I'm away, will you?" she said, smiling.

"I won't." Sylvia smiled back warmly at the older woman, and hugged her. "You go off and have a lovely time. Don't worry about me."

"Of course I'll worry about you, but I'll be back long before it's due." Miss Ebberington had even offered to go along to the hospital when Sylvia's time came.

It was a Friday evening, two days before Miss Ebberington was due to return. For some unknown reason, Sylvia hadn't felt like cooking. She decided to go to the Indian restaurant in Bayswater where Alan had taken her. She had a real craving for Indian food, along with pate and tomatoes. Her mouth watered at the thought of a nice curry.

A waiter brought the menu to her table and then asked if she would like to order any drinks.

"No, thank you," she replied, "but I would like a jug of iced water, please."

She studied the menu before deciding on Chicken Shaslick, which was boneless chicken pieces with tomato, onion and capsicum, marinated with yoghurt and spices and cooked in a clay oven. It was served with salad, and she ordered pilau rice with bombay potatoes.

"No starter?" asked the waiter.

"No starter," she confirmed.

She had just finished her meal and was about to

order a coffee when she experienced the most awful spasm of pain in her lower back. The waiter, aware that something was wrong, came hurrying over.

"Are you all right, Miss? Would you like me to order a taxi?"

"No, thank you. I'll be fine in a minute."

Mindful of how much money a taxi would cost, she decided she would sooner catch the bus. She waited until the pain had receded before paying the bill; then she caught the bus back to the top of her road. As she got off at her stop, another spasm hit her and she almost doubled up. She managed to get safely indoors and undressed before the next one hit her. She sat down on the settee and put her feet up, timing the contractions. They were irregular, but occurred about every ten minutes. She didn't want to spend longer in the hospital than was absolutely necessary. She looked at her watch again. It was nine-fifteen – plenty of time yet. At eleven, she switched the television off and made herself a hot water bottle to take to bed. She reasoned that it might alleviate the pain if she placed it on her back.

During the night, a light powdery snow began to fall. By morning it was snowing heavily. Sylvia had slept fitfully, woken occasionally by further spasms. Her dreams were soiled by images of her father, creeping into her bedroom, taking advantage of her innocence, hurting her. An intense pain wracked her body jolting her into full alertness. She flung her legs outside the bedcovers and stood up to ease her aching back. An even sharper pain hit her and she felt a warm trickle of water run down her legs. She realised from the books she had read that her waters had broken. She quickly threw on a few clothes and walked to the phone box in the hall next door. It was time . . . .

The ambulance arrived within ten minutes. At that moment she wished that Miss Ebberington could have been with her to give her the moral support she felt she so badly needed.

The doctor at the hospital was brisk and efficient. After giving her an internal examination and satisfying himself that the baby was not in a breach position, he asked her what size shoes she took.

Sylvia thought what a daft question this was. Did the baby come out of her foot?

The doctor laughed as she voiced her thoughts. "It's only to give us a rough idea of how big your pelvic muscles are. The larger your feet, the wider your pelvis."

"Oh, I see!" Sylvia found herself laughing, too.

The doctor went on. "I'm going to get the nurse to give you an enema now. That will clear your body of any unwanted waste. After all, you don't want to have an accident on the delivery table, so you?"

The nurse ran a bath for Sylvia and lowered her into the warm water; then with a wet soapy flannel she gave her an all-over wash. That done, she dressed her in a hospital night-gown and left her in the ward, telling her to pull on the bell cord if she needed anything.

Somewhere in the distance, Sylvia heard a clock

chime nine, then ten, then eleven. She had been in the hospital for over twelve hours and in pain for much of that time. A sudden huge pain wracked her body leaving her weak and gasping for breath . . . .

It was not an easy birth. Sylvia thought her body would be ripped in two. It was on the stroke of midnight, on a blustery, bitter day in March, that the little miracle came into the world screaming her protest.

Sylvia slept for a few hours, totally worn out. When she awoke, it was with great tenderness that she reached her hand into the cradle placed by her bedside, and with careful fingers lifted the cover from the sleeping child's face. How beautiful she was! Although only a few hours old, already her black hair was inches long, and when for a fleeting moment she opened her eyes, Sylvia could see that one day they would be just like her father's.

"Sssh, my baby," she whispered, waiting to see the eyes close again in sleep before softly replacing the cover.

The nurse came bustling in. "Is there anything you need? Isn't that a lovely baby! What are you going to call her?"

"I shall call her Bethany," replied Sylvia, which was the first name that came into her mind. She had not allowed herself to think about names until she was sure that it was born healthy.

"That is unusual." The nurse smiled and plumped up the pillows before going out again.

Sylvia thought there was nothing she needed any more. She had everything she had ever wanted. All her